James Billmaier

Beyond Innovation...

inventioneering

Beyond Innovation...

inventioneering

The smartest CEOs will fuse engineering
and invention to dominate the next decade.

James Billmaier
and
Britt Griffith

Published by WindRush Publishers
WindRush Publishers and colophon are trademarks
of WindRush Ventures, LLC

**Text Copyright © 2017 by
James Billmaier and Britt Griffith**
Design & Layout Copyright © 2017
John K. Shipes, Aaron A. Lake & David C. Scott

First Edition 2017

ISBN: 978-098590978-9

Library of Congress Control Number: 2017933032

WindRush Publishers
P.O. Box 670324
Dallas, Texas 75367
www.WindRushPub.com

Printed and bound in the United States of America.

Book design and layout by
John K. Shipes, Aaron A. Lake & David C. Scott

Get informed and inspired at www.WindRushPub.com

Table of Contents

Dedications

To my phenomenal co-author Britt and the amazing people at TurboPatent who are building The TurboPatent Machine...and of course, to my wife Michelle whose patience and understanding allowed me to spend those many weekends pursuing this endeavor.

James Billmaier

To my incredible parents, for their endless love, support, and generosity. To my beloved husband, Brad, for his constant kindness, brilliant input, and boundless encouragement. To my little Raya...I can't wait to meet you. I love the 3 (almost 4) of you more than words can say.

Britt Griffith

And, to those who push the world forward through invention...you rock.

Acknowledgements

I n my experience, nothing good is accomplished without the help of others. Inventioneering is no exception—far from it.

First and foremost, thank you to the TurboPatent team. To David Billmaier, Chad Kirby, Charles Mirho, Byron McCann, and Shane Antos, for their invaluable feedback. To Mark Lee and Rick Jost, for the book's marvelous cover art. And a special thank you to Joe Fortunato and Alex Quant, for their tireless efforts producing the visuals in Inventioneering.

I am so grateful to the Enabling Thought Leadership team. Thank you to Joseph DiNucci, Lauren Cuthbert, Atiya Davidson Dwyer, and Sandi Montour. The ETL team has worked very hard for the past year to make this book great and to keep it on schedule.

Thank you to Michael S. Malone for contributing a fantastic Foreword to Inventioneering. I am honored to be associated with someone so accomplished in the field of technology journalism.

Huge thanks to Mark Lemley, Peter Harter, Britten Sessions, and Brad Griffith for taking time out of their busy schedules to contribute to this project. I deeply value their opinions, and greatly appreciate the insights they provided.

—James Billmaier

> American industry has always had a complicated relationship with intellectual property—patents, trademarks and trade secrets—but never more than now.

Foreword

By Michael S. Malone

On the one hand, it seems as if every day in the news we read about yet another patent dispute between two great corporations, one inevitably reaching new heights in the dollar damages being demanded. On the other hand—especially in places like Silicon Valley, where I work—there is a cliché accepted by many companies (especially startups) that the pace of technological change is so fast, and the patent system so slow, that if and when you are awarded legal protection, the subject of your filing is already obsolete . . . so why go to the trouble and expense?

That last response is in some ways unsurprising. After all, as I write this, two federal courts appear locked in a duel over the implications of a Supreme Court decision on the patentability of computer code (Alice Corp. v. CLS Bank International), each taking an opposing position and seemingly overturning the other's decision on a monthly basis. When even the nation's legal authorities cannot decide what can be patented, why should private companies even try?

Meanwhile, patent "trolls" of every stripe—from seedy lone wolves to professional agencies—roam the landscape using every trick to leverage cash from their corporate targets.

In the face of this myth and chaos, it's not really surprising that many companies seem to have turned their backs on the problem and run away. Or at least handed off all of their IP matters to their legal departments and then prayed that none of the disasters that have befallen other firms will find them.

If there is one overarching message of this book, it's that avoidance—willful ignorance—is a dangerous, even fatal, mistake. You can't run and you can't hide from the Bad Guys of IP, be they individuals or nations; in the Internet age they will find you wherever you are. But even more—which this book goes to great pains to prove— as other forms of competitive edge dissolve in the face of nearinstant global dissemination of ideas, intellectual property is quickly becoming the last business battleground.

The Chinese understand this, which is why in recent years they have made a sudden and stunning reversal from being global patent mavericks to conscientious patent adherents—all as prelude to making IP dominance the centerpiece of their new national competitive initiative. And China is just the beginning. In the years to come, one company, one industry and one nation after another is going to have the epiphany that building and defending their patent portfolios must become a primary building block of their new long-term strategy.

You too will make this discovery.
The only question is: will you do it in time?
That's why this book is so important. Inventioneering is the first book to take a clear-eyed, encompassing look at this new—and dramatically transformed—business environment. In the pages that follow you will likely encounter a complex and sometimes foreboding world filled with millions of players operating under centuries-old rules—rules about which you know next-to-nothing. Yet this new world may

hold the fate of your business in its hands. I know of no better—or faster—way to bring yourself up to speed on this alternative IP universe than this book. For no other reason, it is as a back-grounder and tutorial that you need to read it.

But Inventioneering is much, much more than a briefing document. It is a vision of the future, a roadmap not just to short-term victory in the impending IP Wars, but towards a new way of doing business.

I'll explain what I mean in a minute. But first you must know something about the author of this book.

When it comes to intellectual property, James Billmaier knows what he is talking about: he is the inventor of more than a hundred held or filed patents. Equally important, his career as an entrepreneur, executive and corporate director dates back nearly four decades to include executive positions at such legendary tech companies as Digital Equipment, MIPS (where I first met him), Sun Microsystems and Asymetrix. So he's been on both sides of the table when it comes to talking about inventions and patents.

In 2013, Billmaier founded Seattle-based TurboPatent Corporation. As CEO, James has been a pioneer in bringing the new technology of big data analytics, natural language processing and machine learning to the world of IP invention, application, prosecution and portfolio management. TurboPatent's singular contribution in this field is its version of the "patent machine," described in the final chapters of this book.

With Inventioneering, Billmaier goes one step further. Indeed, in an unprecedented intellectual leap, he follows the implications of this new world to its logical conclusion: that no company can compete for long in a global culture of IP competition by merely bolting a more efficient invention and patent program to its existing business. Rather, to compete and win, companies must change their cultures to exhibit a proactive attitude towards invention and the legal protection of those inventions. In this new culture, the entire executive team clearly understands and aggressively leverages IP as a foundation of their business.

This is what Billmaier means by Inventioneering. And, as he explains in the pages that follow, it is not merely a new corporate function, or something reinforced in the employee manual and regularly updated HR slogans, but is in fact a fundamentally new way of looking at business itself. It is not a "practice," but a cutting-edge method of viewing the enterprise, its purpose and its goals—one that imbues every cubicle and every office in the company, from the most humble lab table to the executive boardroom.

In fact, the boardroom most of all. Because as Billmaier consistently reminds us in the following pages, a revolution this profound and complete—and especially one that must take place this quickly—can only begin in the boardroom and must be reflected in every action that the board, the CEO and the executive team take thereafter. And that is why, though Billmaier addresses this book to all readers and to all employees of a company, it is to the board and executive row that he particularly targets his message.

For a book about a subject as reputedly dry as the business and law of intellectual property, Inventioneering is a shocking read. And once you fully comprehend its message, it should prove electrifying. James Billmaier has given you an extraordinary gift: he has not only given you a glimpse of your competitive future but also the recipe for emerging victorious in that future.

This is what makes Inventioneering immensely valuable . . . but only if you read it carefully, heed its warnings, learn its lessons—and act. You won't need to tell the world that you did so. It will be obvious.

Michael S. Malone
Sunnyvale, California

Michael S. Malone is one of the world's leading technology business journalists. The author of more than twenty award-winning books, he is currently Dean's Executive Professor at Santa Clara University and an Associate Fellow of Said Business School at Oxford University.

During my early Internet days as the vice president and general manager of Sun Microsystems' Network Software Division, our sage co-founder and CEO, Scott McNealy, would challenge us to work with our management and technical teams to invent a business capable of killing our existing business.

Introduction

McNealy's motto was, "Eat Lunch or Be Lunch," by which he meant that if you could figure out how to break through your market barriers and annihilate your own market position in the ever-changing and rapidly accelerating business world of the early 1990s, your competition probably could too.

The Internet changed everything. But that was just the initial jolt. Today there are new and radical changes underway that are transforming the very nature of business competition. And these changes will leave no company untouched.

Sustainable business success comes from a combination of things: It comes from delivering a compelling product or service that allows you to capture initial market share. It comes from understanding and reacting to continual market and technological shifts. And finally, it comes from defending your company's gains by erecting barriers to market entry from competitors.

Simply put, to avoid being lunch, you must successfully defend your position. And to do that you must build ever-stronger barriers.

Experience has shown that these barriers to market entry take two forms:

A. Operational Barriers—The traditional proactive and competitive means corporations take to protect themselves—i.e., the day-to-day line operations that keep the company speeding ahead of the competition: research and development, design, manufacturing, marketing, distribution, and sales and customer services, as well as such staff activities as recruiting.

B. Legal Barriers—Regulatory tools (including patents, trade secrets, trademarks and brands) that have nothing to do with a company's ongoing need to spring ahead of the competition, but rely instead on a perimeter of legal defense to fend off competitors. Legal barriers come courtesy of governmental grants, which reward a company for making investments that lead to inventive break-throughs. They also differ from operational barriers in that legal barriers are designed to stand for years, thus encouraging and rewarding innovative investment.

Historically, legal barriers have taken a back seat to operational barriers. After all, the business of business is competition. Traditionally, companies are organized to do battle with their competitors over products, markets and customers. But much of the justification for this preference can only be attributed to inertia and, certainly, the logic behind it no longer holds. In 1975, just four decades ago, only 20 percent of corporate value was attributed to intangible assets. Today, that number has been inverted, with 80 percent of corporate value now attributed to these intangible assets. This

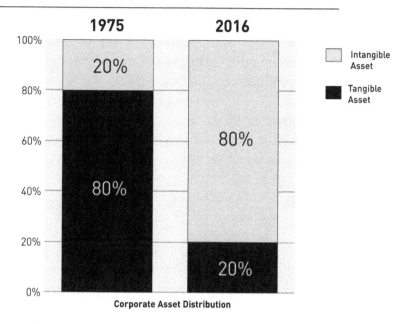

Tangible vs Intangible Corporate Value

In 1975, only 20 percent of corporate value was attributed to intangible assets. Today, that number has been inverted, with 80 percent of corporate value now attributed to intangible assets.

is reflected in the fact that there are now 40 million American jobs that depend upon intellectual property (IP). It also is well documented that market valuation multiples are higher for companies with strong, protected IP. Thus, US companies in IP-intensive industries today generate more than $5 trillion in economic activity per year and are responsible for three quarters of all US exports.

This is not a trend that will reverse or even abate anytime soon. Goods that could be effortlessly digitized, such as books and music, were easy pickings for disruption. The cost of production and distribution of these informational products dropped nearly to zero with the advent of such Internet companies as Amazon and Apple. Today, with recent advancements in 3D printing, bio-printers, robotics, open source software, reverse engineering techniques, industrial cyber-theft, etc., we are at the onset of an era in which physical objects will undergo the same disruption as did the informational and media products that preceded them.

Think about it: Products that hold some competitive protection by the sheer complexity of their manufacturing are now turned into digital files that can be shared around the world and recreated anywhere. The result is what Deven R. Desai, of the Georgia Institute of Technology—Scheller College of Business, and Gerard N. Magliocca, professor at the Indiana University Robert H. McKinney School of Law, called the "Napsterization" of all things in a 2013 abstract entitled "Patents, Meet Napster: 3D Printing and the Digi-talization of Things."

So here's the problem: Any advantage offered by a strategy of operational barriers has either vanished or is about to do so. What proved to be decisive in the twentieth century is essentially inconsequential in the twenty-first. The advantages once held by big companies have disappeared.

Operational vs Legal Barriers

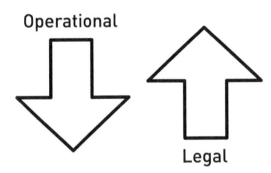

Operational

Legal

Competitive advantages achieved through operational barriers are vanishing. As a result, the importance of legal barriers is increasing.

Thanks to the technology revolution, any company, no matter how small, can now deliver world-class product development, manufacturing, marketing, distribution and service through Amazon, Google, 3D printing, automated outsourced manufacturing, open source software, and a host of other global services and intermediaries.

If your competitors can't figure out how to design what you do, they will probably figure out how to copy or steal it, and from that point on, manufacturing, marketing and distribution are all just commodity services. We have entered an era in which operational barriers alone are rapidly falling to fast followers. Why would your competition do all the hard and expensive work of innovation when they can monitor and replicate your work for pennies on the dollar?

In other words, whatever your competitive advantages have been until now, they are soon going away. Probably forever. So, to stay ahead—indeed, to stay alive—what do you do?

You turn to the one remaining protection against those who would simply copy the competitive advantage you earned through expensive research and development: the legal barrier offered by patents, trade secrets, and the various other bulwarks of intellectual property.

Smart, forward-looking enterprises are doing just that; so, too, are forward-looking nations, most notably China, as we will see. That means it is very likely that at least one of your competitors has already embarked on just such an IP strategy and will soon have some deadly surprises awaiting you.

The future of competition is becoming clear: In this new competitive era, where product is reduced to information, and that information is the embodiment of the company's innovation, those who create a superior intellectual property strategy, and execute on it, will ultimately win. Meanwhile, most C-Suite executives will be caught unprepared, reduced to watching dumbfounded as those smart enough to play a few moves ahead emerge victorious.

The prospect of this reality, and of what the future holds, should worry you. And if you are like most corporate executives, who think about IP only when faced with the threat of being sued, you should be terrified. Adding to the peril is the fact that new IP threats are constantly emerging. For example, activist shareholders armed with patent knowledge are now holding boards and executive management teams responsible for their mismanagement of the company's IP portfolio, or are seeking to invalidate a company's critical patents after taking a short position on the company's stock.

The sad truth is that outside of their legal departments, most American companies (and the people who run them) have insufficient knowledge of intellectual property—of its creation, its management, and its potential strategic, financial and operational use. That is the bad news because, as noted above, there is no question that at least one of your competitors is IP savvy and is already figuring out how to use their superior knowledge of the system to defeat you.

A global corporate intellectual property war has begun and most business leaders are unaware that they are even vulnerable. If you are one of those leaders and the time comes to defend yourself, you will have no factual basis to argue that you were hit with a surprise attack. So know this now: you have been warned.

But here's the good news: The information C-Suite executives need to survive the coming IP war isn't held in secret; it isn't locked away in an underground vault. Essential education is readily available and a path to survival awaits you. The next move, however, is yours.

This book is designed to provide the data and details you need to create a dominant twenty-first-century plan. We will begin by outlining the current and impending threats so you can better assess the urgency and gravity of your circumstance. We will then translate and simplify the complex world of IP as it exists today, which will provide you with a foundation of IP business fundamentals. Next, we'll look at prescient leaders and the companies and nations they run that have already developed sophisticated and coordinated IP strategies and are on the move.

Finally, we will take you a step further, a step beyond achieving parity with your competitors. This book will reveal how IP can evolve in your company from merely being a perfunctory legal exercise and an underused asset to a competitive imperative and differentiating advantage—and ultimately a cornerstone of your corporate culture. This is what we call Inventioneering. First, however, you must understand one immutable fact: For your company to survive and to thrive, the Invention-eering initiative must start at the very top—in the board room, at executive staff strategy meetings, and ultimately, with the CEO. It is critical that you, as a leader of your company, read this book because that cultural transforma-tion cannot simply be bolted onto the organization by your legal department or put in place by executive fiat. Rather, it must be driven and modeled by a company's leadership, beginning with the chairman of the board and the CEO.

The impending IP war is not an optional war. It is not one that you will be able to escape. As a result, you have a choice to make: drive the steamroller or become part of the road.

It is our goal that by the time you finish this book, you will know where, when, and how to fight. And fight to win.

Beyond Innovation...

inventioneering

> Economics is based on scarcity. Things are valuable because they are scarce. The more abundant they become, the cheaper they become. But a series of technological changes is underway that promises to end scarcity as we know it for a wide variety of goods.
>
> —Mark Lemley

Chapter 1

The End of Scarcity

I n the story of mankind, scarcity is the antagonist. And civilization is the twenty-millennia-long tale of the struggle to overcome that scarcity. Perpetual shortages of food, water, arable land, medicine, safe shelter and education filled that history—right up to the present—with endless examples of devastating famine, internecine strife, plague, drought and other natural disasters, and all-round deprivation.

But beginning in the middle of the twentieth century and accelerating into the twenty-first century, an extraordinary and historic change has begun, one that is overturning the tyranny of scarcity endemic to the last twenty thousand years. Thanks to Moore's Law, the Internet, breakthroughs in manufacturing (including in robotics) and stunning advances in science and medicine emerging from research laboratories, we appear to be entering an era free of these previous sources of scarcity. Indeed, some are even suggesting a coming Age of Abundance.

One expert who has followed this trend is Mark Lemley, the William H. Neukom Professor of Law at Stanford Law School, and the director of the Stanford Program in Law, Science and Technology. For Lemley, the Internet points the way towards this future world of abundance. In an essay entitled "IP in a World Without Scarcity," he argues that the Internet has "reduced the cost of production and distribution of informational content effectively to zero."

Lemley also notes how the Internet has changed the ways in which information is distributed, in particular by separating the creators of content from the distributors. The latter now transmit information for free, or almost free, and they don't much care about the nature of the content they are distributing. "So the Internet has not only slashed the cost of creation, production and distribution," Lemley writes, "it has also disaggregated creation and distribution."

But this is only the beginning, he continues, because the Internet itself serves as the platform for other emerging technologies that can springboard off the web's unprecedented reach and speed. Now, a host of new technologies promises to do for physical goods (and many services) what the Internet did for information. As examples, Lemley points to:

- 3D Printers – "print" physical objects from digital designs and manufacture physical goods based on any digital design
- Synthetic Biology – automation of the manufacture of custom-made gene sequences, allowing anyone to create a gene sequence that can be sent to a company that will "print" it using the basic building blocks of genetics
- Robotics – allows many services currently provided by humans to be offered for free by programmed general-purpose machines

"Combine these four developments—the Internet, 3D printing, robotics, and synthetic biology," Lemley notes, "and it is entirely plausible to envision a not-too-distant world in which most things that people want can be downloaded and created on site for very little money—essentially the cost of raw materials."

Futurist Jeremy Rifkin calls this "the zero marginal cost" society. Author and entrepreneur Peter Diamandis calls it the "coming age of abundance," as does popular science writer Michio Kaku and economist Brink Lindsey. And even if all of mankind's historic scarcities are never completely overcome, enough scarcity will be overcome to transform daily human life—and the global economy, in particular—in the decades to come.

Let's look a bit closer at just one of the technologies that is already contributing to "the zero marginal cost" society. Consider the impact of robots on manufacturing. According to a recent University of Oxford study titled "The Future of Employment," industrial robots with machine vision and precise dexterity are dropping in cost at an accelerating rate, and are projected to be available to a significant portion of manufacturing operations within the next few years. Ron Potter, director of robotics technology for Factory Automation Systems, Inc., calculates that the average cost to operate a medium-sized, industrial robot deployed for material handling applications costs about 75 cents per hour to operate. Compared to human labor at $15 to $20 per hour, the financial case for robotics is clear.

To illustrate: The Changying Precision Technology Company factory in China recently replaced approximately 90 percent of its human workforce (650 employees) with robots, and has already experienced a 162.5 percent increase in production. As a result, the number of human employees is expected to drop to just twenty in the near future.

The productivity of robots as compared to humans, combined with their declining cost, means greater adoption across a multitude of industries. In fact, the same Oxford study predicts that 41 percent of current employment categories have a "high probability" of being eliminated due to robotics, computerization and other technology. The result is a widespread decrease in the cost of manufacturing pretty much every physical thing. Anyone—anywhere, anytime—will have access to low-cost production. The competitive barrier to entry in manufacturing is rapidly vanishing.

It is human nature to believe that today's effective tools will continue to work in the future—even if that future is radically transformed. But in fact, history has shown that atti-tude to almost always be wrong. You can be certain that the way we do everything, from governing our country to conducting commerce to going about our daily existence, is going to change—and change profoundly—in ways we cannot yet even imagine.

One of the goals of this book is to show you that this change is not only coming, but that it has already begun. And that the once-strong and enduring walls currently crumbling are the operational defenses of day-to-day business activities and practices that we have long depended upon to protect us from the predations of competitors.

Why? Because, ironically, many of the operational barriers companies have devised over the last three centuries—mass customization, supply chain management, subscriptions, monopolies and trusts, warranties, exclusivity, corporate laboratories and high R&D budgets—were designed specifically to reinforce scarcity. These barriers both limited the choices consumers had in their purchases and held off potential competitors who lacked the resources to produce, market or distribute comparable products and services.

Meanwhile, the limitations (scarcity) of communications and distribution meant that established companies could operate with little worry about competitors popping up in distant markets and challenging them at home.

All of that has now changed.

The first glimpse of what was to come arrived at the very end of the twentieth century, in June 1999—the early days of the World Wide Web—when Napster first appeared on the scene. Creators Shawn Fanning and Sean Parker, being children of their time, saw something their elders did not: that a new digital audio technology known as MP3 allowed the creation of music files that could be swapped among users without having to go through traditional retail channels—i.e., they could be swapped for free.

Two years later, Napster had twenty-six million users and the service was the hottest phenomenon in the digital world. Napster's quick rise was a lesson in the extreme scalability of the web, a lesson that wasn't lost on the founders of Facebook and Twitter. It also drove the music industry insane, as it watched its revenues plummet as millions of college kids and high schoolers stopped buying CDs and instead simply traded music files with one another.

From the music industry's panic ensued poorly conceived legal actions. They sued little Napster and shut it down—a small, ultimately insignificant victory in a much larger war. The technology to freely share music had reached a point of no return, causing the industry's revenue streams to collapse. Looking back, what might have been had those who controlled the top artists' content embraced the future?

What the music industry and other companies should have learned from the Napster era was that technological innovation, especially when tied to the speed of delivery and the near-zero incremental cost of adding new users made possible by broadband Internet, was about to make all of the traditional operational barriers obsolete. That the Napsterization of the global economy—digitalization and instant and frictionless delivery everywhere—would not only spell the end of scarcity, but would also mark an explosion of competition. Which is exactly what happened. Indeed, the revolutionary effects of technological innovation make up the first chapter in the story of doing business in the twenty-first century.

The old business tools and strategies for competing in a marketplace characterized by scarcity are quickly becoming obsolete. So, the question now: What replaces them? And if new and dangerous competition is springing up quickly in the most unlikely places, how do we recognize it? And even if we do recognize that competition, how do we meet and defeat it using competitive advantage? Finally, what does that advantage even look like?

The answer, as we'll see in the next few chapters, comes from another, older—and often ignored—corner of the business world.

> In the summer of 1979, at an industry conference in Silicon Valley before the giants of the chip industry—Intel, Fairchild and National Semiconductor, among others—a lanky red-haired Hewlett-Packard executive with a casual manner named Ed Hayes dropped on the US semiconductor industry one of the biggest bombs in American business history.

Chapter 2

Echoes of the Past

T he firms in attendance, some of the most important in the US electronics sector and critical players in the nation's economy, chose to attend the conference because HP was still among the most important, innovative and admired companies in tech—and a major purchaser of integrated circuit chips. Anything said by an executive from the notably reticent HP deserved attention.

Hayes' presentation began predictably enough, according to Michael S. Malone in his book The Microprocessor: A Biography. Working with an overhead projector, Hayes put up a series of slides showing annual chip orders by his company, their product types and vendors. Standard stuff.

"[Hayes] opened by explaining that HP purchased in volume several hundred thousand components each year from outside manufacturers for use in its various computers, calculators and instruments," Malone wrote. "Most of these devices were bought from US manufacturers, he continued, but a few were purchased from some of the big Japanese electronics firms: NEC, Hitachi, Fujitsu, Toshiba and Mitsubishi."

Fair enough. The chip executives in the audience knew that the Japanese had been fabricating computer chips for some time, and though they still owned little market share, it stood to reason that a company like HP might buy a few of their devices at a bargain price, or for specialty applications.

But then Hayes put up the next slide. And even before he could begin to speak, a murmur arose from the audience. This slide compared the quality of US chips bought by HP versus those purchased from Japan. The numbers were shocking: Whereas HP typically had to return as much as 5 percent of purchased US chips, the return rate of comparable Japanese chips was almost zero. The chip executives looked at each other in disbelief. It had taken them twenty years to bring yield rates up from 10 percent to more than 90 percent, and they thought themselves miracle workers for having done so. Now, the Japanese, long the butt of jokes thanks to consumer products that were perceived as cheap and shoddy, had not just caught up to them, but had surpassed them. How was this even possible?

Hayes wasn't done, however. With the next slide, according to Malone, he dropped another bombshell:

"What's more, initial Japanese deliveries were always on time, and any replacements were made immediately. By comparison, he continued, US chips were usually delivered late, replacements were sometimes made with equally faulty chips, and the claiming customer, HP, was typically treated as if it should feel lucky to be getting any replacements at all."

Implicit in Hayes' words was the message that henceforth, Hewlett-Packard Co., the most admired technology company on the planet, would be buying its chips from the Japanese . . . and if US chipmakers didn't shape up, and shape up fast, they would lose not only HP's, but the rest of the world's business as well.

The men who had walked into the room earlier that day had been smugly complacent, secure in the knowledge that they were the captains of the most valuable and fastest-growing industry on earth. Within an hour, however, they had been reduced to panic at the vision of their entire world disappearing under the competitive onslaught from companies located thousands of miles away, companies they knew little about. What frightened them the most was not just that the Japanese chips were of higher quality, or that their Japanese counterparts provided better service—or even that the Japanese chips were also up to 10 percent cheaper . . . but that they were all three things at the same time.

The US semiconductor industry, facing potential annihilation, had no idea how to respond. Thus began the great US-Japanese chip war, which consumed most of the 1980s. It would take years, and billions of dollars of lost revenue, before the US chip business regained its industry leadership. By then, Silicon Valley, which had long prided itself on its independence, had jumped into the federal government's arms, surrendering its freedom and begging for protection.

Looking back after more than thirty years, it is now possible to put this whole story into perspective. The Japanese weren't superhuman after all; they were just forward-looking, focused and committed. Their chip industry, backed by the Japanese government, recognized that integrated circuits, including the new generation of microprocessors, were going to become the linchpin of the world's economy—they would ultimately be embedded by the billions into every corner of modern life. If Japan was going to maintain its historic growth and remain at the center of this new (digital) economy, it was going to have to beat the American chip companies at their own game. To do so, Japan decided to play a different game—one aligned with its own strengths.

Japan's game-changing advantage had, ironically, come some thirty years earlier from an American business theorist named W. Edwards Deming. Deming, who felt himself a prophet without honor at home in the US, had gone to Japan after World War II, where his ideas found a much better reception. In fact, many in Japan credit Deming's theories with inspiring the nation's so-called post-war economic miracle from 1950 to 1960, a boom period that launched Japan on its path to becoming the world's second largest economy, a title it held for more than forty years. Due to Deming's contributions to Japan's reputation for high-quality products and its economic power, he is renowned for having had more impact on modern Japanese business than any other individual not of Japanese heritage.

The transformational message Deming brought to Japan was that of focusing the organization on quality vs cost as a key competitive factor. Conversely, US companies managed by the financial numbers and had always thought of quality as an incidental factor added to products by checking them at the end of the assembly line. Deming, however, taught that quality was built into products from their very design, and then throughout all of the company's established processes in terms of designing, building, selling and supporting the products. Those companies that transformed their cultures and fully embraced the Deming philosophy not only experienced a dramatic increase in product quality, but also, ironically, saw a reduction in overall costs.

$$\text{Quality} = \frac{\text{Results of work efforts}}{\text{Total costs}}$$

As noted in Wikipedia, Deming's philosophy was summarized by some of his Japanese proponents in the 1970s with the following "a" versus "b" comparison:

(a) – When people and organizations focus primarily on quality, defined by the following ratio, quality tends to increase, and costs fall over time.
(b) – However, when people and organizations focus primarily on costs, costs tend to rise, and quality declines over time.

The Japanese executives who led their companies through the philosophical and cultural shift to what's known as Total Quality quickly revolutionized entire industries, including, notably, the semiconductor industry. The US semiconductor industry was reduced to standing by and watching helplessly as Japanese chipmakers carved great chunks out of the memory chip business, leaving what remained to them all but unprofitable. Even mighty Intel, formerly the world's largest memory chip maker, eventually had to abandon the business and retreat into the much more difficult microprocessor business in the hopes of surviving.

In the end, it would prove a close-run thing—and, one would hope, a lesson in eternal vigilance. The Japanese attack on the US semiconductor industry taught us that at any moment, a competitor could shift the game, target a weak spot and destroy or dramatically impact the current industry incumbents. And once a field is lost, it takes an almost superhuman effort to regain leadership.

Ultimately, the lesson of the great chip war of the 1980s was that your biggest threat will not come from those competitors who match your strengths and your areas of focus, but from those who attack where you are weakest, and in those operations you take for granted.

The organizational and executive level parallels between product quality prior to the 1980s and current-day attitudes toward intellectual property are stunning: The isolation of the function. The acceptance of afterthought. The hardened organizational boundaries. And worst of all, the lack of knowledge and leadership at the executive level.

Could it be that your competitors might embrace intellectual property in the same way Deming taught the Japanese semiconductor companies to embrace Total Quality? Could your competitors assimilate intellectual property into their very culture and then use it as a weapon to disrupt your market position?

They already have.

Just such an attack, one greater and more far-reaching than anything attempted in the 1980s by Japan, is already underway. The first shots have been fired. And yet, other than its earliest victims, few companies seem to realize the existence, much less the magnitude, of this attack.

This time around the existential threat comes not from Japan but from China, which has just undergone a breathtaking change from being a pirate intellectual-property economy to one dedicated to owning the world's largest IP portfolio. The emerging fight will be over which nation dominates competitive knowledge for the remainder of the twenty-first century. It is not a war we dare lose.

Chapter 3

Meet Your New and Enhanced Competitor

A s with the Japanese electronics industry's assault in the late 1970s, this challenge is currently taking place beneath a relatively placid surface, awaiting that moment when it will suddenly burst through the surface and leave the opposition with no time to respond. And this time, even more than before, if you wait too long, the risks to your enterprise will become enormous and your chance of success low. And should you somehow emerge victorious, that victory will have come as a result of massive sacrifice and financial loss.

Even as the traditional operational barriers that companies have effectively erected over the last century begin to crumble, there still remains an even older, less-often used line of defense. We've noted it in passing, but now you may be starting to recognize and appreciate its real value.

Intellectual property.

If that term makes you shudder and shake your head, it is probably for good reason. For many decades now, IP has been the equivalent of the ax mounted in the wall behind a small window pane and beneath a sign reading, "In Case of Emergency Break Glass."

Well, that emergency has now arrived.
It's time to break the glass.

But before you do that, it is time for an attitude change.
If you feel a certain revulsion regarding IP, you're not alone.
Most company executives, especially those at the C-level,
have had only bad experiences regarding patents. It usually
begins with the process of filing for patents. That is, dealing
with patent attorneys, the Pharisees of IP, who tease filings
out of a few notes from your engineering department and
then charge you a small fortune to file multiple applications
in multiple countries. Then, other than writing regular
checks, nothing seems to ever happen. At best, years
later, you get a sheet of paper giving you the patent on a
technology that's now obsolete or no longer part of your
strategy. And that's the good part of dealing with IP.

The bad part is when you get sued—by unknown
competitors, obscure inventors, patent trolls and an array of
other strange creatures who seem to exclusively inhabit the
IP universe and who demand insane amounts of damages,
try to shut down your operations or try to force you to
pay an outrageous licensing fee. Attempt to fight them
and your case gets smeared all over the media—thereby
frightening investors and customers and driving down
your stock price—and the court case drags on for years,
comparable to Jarndyce v. Jarndyce in Charles Dickens'
Bleak House. After all the distraction and expense, it
then either ends with a whimper or a ruling so obscene
that you have to start the whole process all over again.

You probably think we're being a bit hyperbolic
here. We wish that were the case. As anyone who has
ever suffered through a nasty patent fight can tell you,
including T.J. Rodgers, the founder and CEO of Cypress
Semiconductor, who over the last thirty years has fought

every frivolous patent suit to the bitter end by refusing to settle. (He is also known for wallpapering his office with the losing complaint documents of his adversaries.) Too many companies, however, do settle; they write a check and hope the problem will go away—all the while knowing that it won't, since other predators will only be more motivated by the possibility of payment.

Your attitude towards intellectual property probably lies somewhere within this spectrum: you either see it as an expensive nuisance or a special kind of nightmare. Well, your attitude has to change. IP is the new battlefield, and you need to learn to be the best kind of a warrior in this new competition. And you must begin by no longer seeing IP as an unwanted burden but instead as both a strategic and tactical advantage—and not just for defense, but for offense as well.

There is one other reason why you must develop a twenty-first century IP strategy. If our argument thus far hasn't persuaded you, then this should: Some of your competitors have recognized this seismic shift in business competition and, as you read this, are already embracing new and sweeping IP strategies. And that's just your industry neighbors. Entire nations are also awakening to the importance of putting into place national IP initiatives. And none has awakened sooner and committed itself more deeply to IP as the new competitive edge than China, the world's second largest economy.

We'll look at the domestic threat from IP later in the book. For now, let's examine the immense threat building in China.

There are disturbing commonalities between Japan's assault on the electronics industry in the 1970s and China's emerging global strategy today. As in the 1970s, when Japan was dismissed as a toymaker at worst and an unsophisticated copier at best, China is still largely seen as a global patent pirate. In reality, in recent years China has morphed into one of the most legalistic patent accumulators on the planet, complete with a long-term strategy that features a strong alliance between government and industry.

For those of you who still dismiss China's patents as poorly written crap barely worth the paper they are printed on, you are partially correct. At the same time, let us remind you of the almost laughable Japanese automobiles of the early 1970s. This is how it starts. As we will discuss later in this book, a patent allows the holder to stop others from making, using, selling, offering to sell, or importing products or services that incorporate or require the invention. So, if your company is planning to sell something into the second largest economy on the planet, to make a product in the most advanced manufacturing country on the planet, or incorporate a part from China, then you had better take this seriously. We assure you that China is.

But there is also a big difference between Japan of the '70s and China today. Japan was only targeting a single— albeit huge and prosperous—market sector. China is preparing to make its move on the entire global economy, an action that will affect every nation, and America most of all. And it isn't focusing on end products such as computer chips, but on the entire root of intellectual property that is the wellspring of the US economy.

China's transformation to an IP powerhouse is there for anyone to see. But beyond the generally accepted, and now inaccurate, reputation of China as a country that disregards IP, few people are looking closely.

The China we think we know—a place of cloned consumer products, stolen international trade secrets and a general lawlessness regarding any form of IP—was already becoming an anachronism in the 1980s. Recognizing that the benefits of being a patent and trademark outlaw were beginning to work against its desire to be a global economic power, the People's Republic of China joined the World Intellectual Property Organization (WIPO) in 1980. Then, in 1984, China signed the Paris Convention for the Protection of Industrial Property, and a year later, the Madrid Agreement for the International Registration of Trademarks.

China has followed this pattern of a being a good international citizen regarding patents and trademarks ever since, even rewriting its IP laws to correspond to the global Agreement on Trade-Related Aspects of Intellectual Property Rights (TRIPS). All of this culminated in 1992 with China entering into a memorandum of understanding (MoU) with the United States government to provide copyright protection for all American "works," with the nonbonding agreement becoming a full agreement in 1995.

In other words, at least on paper, the PRC has been a good global citizen regarding intellectual property now for more than thirty years. In fact, by Chinese law, these international agreements actually supersede any Chinese IP law in court.

The reality, however, is not so shiny. In large regions of the country, actual enforcement of these agreements is spotty at best (the country didn't even begin training IP enforcement officers until 1996). Thus, many copycats and counterfeiters across the country still don't know they are violating the law. Moreover, when illegal behavior helps the national economy—as with the government-sponsored search engine, Baidu—the governing party is often willing to look the other way.

Meanwhile, the Chinese courts have become much more willing to uphold international patent and trademark law, accepting litigation from companies in other nations against their Chinese competitors. While the verdicts have largely proven to be fair, there remains a bias against awarding meaningful monetary judgments, or even issuing restraining orders against Chinese companies. Most notoriously, in 1992 a convicted Chinese patent infringer was fined just $252 against an estimated $30 million in losses to Microsoft.

All of this led the Office of the United States Trade Representatives in 2014 to once again place China on its "priority watch list"—as well as to file two claims against China with the World Trade Organization over IP violations and restraint of market access.

For China, these recent episodes have been minor setbacks in what has been a historic turnaround in little more than a quarter century from being an international IP renegade to becoming a key player in international patent agreements. Needless to say, China didn't go through the enormously expensive and disruptive cultural dislocation out of goodwill. Rather, it recognized earlier than most nations, including the US, that the next big competitive war would be fought over the legal ownership of ideas. Seeing this potential strategic advantage, combined with a pliant but official legal system and armies of newly trained patent specialists, China decided to go all in and make IP world dominance a full national initiative. And for most of this decade, it has assiduously pursued that goal.

In June of 2016 the The Wall Street Journal ran an article headlined "China Bites Apple." A Beijing court upheld a patent infringement suit filed by a tiny Chinese company against Apple and the court enforced an injunction restricting Apple's sales of two iPhone models. As a result, Carl Icahn sold his $5 billion stake in Apple, saying he was worried that Beijing will "make it very difficult for Apple to sell there."

What is astonishing, and terrifying, is that few American executives, industry and academic researchers, diplomats and government officials have even noticed this emerging threat. We read of the exploding numbers of patent filings in China, which now surpass even those filed in the US, and the larger implications of this news doesn't seem to register. We watch as China has grown to become the world's second largest economy and fail to draw any conclusions about what this one-two punch means. And when we hear from our industry counterparts about how China has suddenly become the most litigious patent economy ever, it fails to register in our minds how this is the third crucial step, enabling China to protect its own economy while storming the rest of the world's knowledge base.

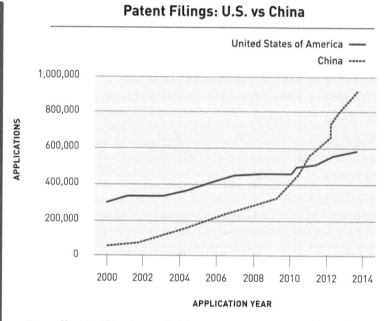

Patent Filings: U.S. vs China

United States of America ——
China -----

Patent filings in China have exploded in recent years, surpassing the number of filings in the U.S.

Most of all, we haven't drawn the final, devastating conclusion that once China has positioned itself as the world's dominant player in intellectual property it can, at its own discretion and on its own timetable, convert that knowledge base into real products and services, holding off potential international competition as it does so.

Incredibly, this bold strategy is the stated policy of the Chinese government. Just ask any US company facing a potential acquisition by a Chinese company, or a tech startup looking for funding from a Chinese investor. Notably, over the last two years the beginning and end points of all negotiations have seemed to revolve around intellectual property: How complete is your patent portfolio? What is the status of your filings? These have become the vital, even decisive, questions now being asked by Chinese acquirers and investors. It is a question they have been told to ask— and for the right answer, they are amply rewarded.

All of this is not to cast blame on China's strategic national patent initiative. On the contrary. Like Japan at the end of the twentieth century (Total Quality) and Great Britain at the end of the eighteenth century (the Industrial Revolution), China has found a strategy—intellectual property law—by which it can leverage its own inventions and/or cultural strengths to steal a march on its biggest global competitors. Had each of the above nations not chosen not to pursue this strategy, they would have betrayed their citizens.

No, the real blame lies with those nations which, faced with these historic threats, failed—through ignorance, arrogance or lack of leadership—to respond promptly, intelligently and decisively to the emerging threat. China is making its move not just because it sees its own advantages, but also because it perceives a growing weakness in Europe, and especially in the US, when it comes to protecting competitive interests. China is pouncing because we are in retreat or because we are, at best, inert.

No nation that wants to compete in the global marketplace for the remainder of the twenty-first century dares to ignore what is taking place with intellectual property in China. And that is especially true for the United States. If, as with Japan a quarter century ago, we refuse to take the Chinese IP threat seriously, if we choose to continue to compete for the global marketplace using obsolete tools, or if, under challenges from lawmakers, courts or predators, our patent system slackens just as China's grows more disciplined, we will quickly fall behind.

On the other hand, if American industry can just respond to this threat promptly, in a coordinated way, and with the alignment of the immense resources and cultural advantages held by this nation, it can meet this economic threat—and defeat it—with minimal damage to our society, our economy and (not least) your company. And make no mistake, your company is directly involved in this battle.

US companies can win. However, we cannot wait for the government or the courts to join the fight. We must start now. We must meet the IP challenge from China and at home by preparing ourselves, company by company. And not just by expanding and protecting our own IP portfolios, but by looking beyond this present conflict towards another, bigger, playing field, where American ingenuity and practical thinking—our history as a society of tinkerers—gives us a natural, inherent advantage. But don't look or wait for some collective, coordinated nationwide program. Each company must act individually.

Further, we must start at the top: in the boardrooms and executive offices of the nation's corporations great and small, and among America's thought leaders. And we must be prepared to reorient the culture of our enterprises around a different approach to intellectual property and its application; that is, to expand beyond indeterminate innovation towards systemic invention.

We call this new strategic, offensive, and ultimately optimistic and inclusive approach to IP Inventioneering. And we believe it will be crucial to competitive success in the global economy for the rest of this century.

We will spend the rest of this book explaining Inventioneering—how it works and how it can be implemented. For now, it is important to understand that it rests on the following tenets:

- If you want your business to survive, you had better embrace IP. There is no other option.
- If you want your business to thrive, you need to go much further than just filing a bunch of "cover-your-ass" patents the night before the product launch.
- Creating and protecting high value patents and trade secrets is not something that can be bolted onto your organization. It, and the IP it produces, must be embedded and absorbed into the very heart of your corporate culture.

Just as Deming taught the Japanese that quality must be far more than a final step at the end of a manufacturing process (Total Quality), Inventioneering is the Total Quality of IP.

Our ultimate goal with this book is to teach you an enhanced approach to product development that embraces IP and that will impact corporations in a manner that will not only enable you to endure the impending global IP war, but also to become the leader in your industry and position yourself to dominate in the new global economy that will emerge thereafter.

In the pages that follow, our task is to open your eyes and those of the key decision-makers in your organization—boards of directors, C-level executives and major investors, as well as venture capitalists, academics and elected officials—to the intellectual property threat emerging from both China and at home, and to offer a real strategy for individual enterprises and the United States as a nation to respond. The good news is that in doing so, we will position your company and the nation for even greater long-term economic success.

But that is in the future. For now, let this book be a call to arms. Time is running short.

> Brace yourself, because in this chapter we intend to scare you with some business stories that may be more frightening than anything you'll see on a movie screen.

Chapter 4

Litigation, Trolls & Tolls

Here's how it usually works: Your company is humming along, enjoying good growth, strong profits and ever-greater market share. Investors are happy and driving up your stock price. The business press writes promising stories about your company's prospects and glowing tales about your leadership and vision. Things just can't get much better, and as you look around at the budding enterprise you've created, you take satisfaction in the fact that your dreams for the company, for its employees and for yourself have come true. . .

And then one sunny morning, like an ICBM coming unseen over the North Pole, you receive a notification that your company is being sued for a vast sum of money for patent infringement. You look at the name on the complaint, expecting to see one of your competitors and making a mental note to schedule what will likely be a rational cross-licensing discussion. But you don't recognize the name; indeed, you can't even find it on the Internet. Who are these guys?

And that's when the nightmare begins.

BlackBerry, Black Eye

Consider the story of Research In Motion (RIM), the company behind the BlackBerry mobile communication devices. In 2000, RIM and a number of other companies in the telecommunications industry were served notice that they were in violation of key wireless email patents, and were being offered the opportunity to license those patents from NTP Inc. for $10 million. While Microsoft, AT&T and others agreed to NTP's licensing terms, RIM's co-CEOs made a decision to fully contest the validity of the patents both legally and in the courts of public opinion. This would prove to be a horrific mistake—a C-Suite intellectual property misstep so egregious that the company would never recover. As a result, RIM (now called BlackBerry), the one-time leader in the smartphone market, retains only a tiny share and, ironically, is now asserting its own patents in a desperate effort to make money.

NTP was originally a pager company whose forward prospects were crushed by the combined forces of the Internet and cell phones. With the market need for a separate paging device decimated, NTP's remaining valuable asset, a powerful portfolio of fifty US patents, was licensed to an obscure Virginia-based holding company whose mission was to obtain licensees.

In fact, NTP no longer made anything. It became a "non-practicing entity" (NPE) or a "patent assertion entity" (PAE) and existed primarily to enforce its valuable intellectual property against successful operating product companies that it asserted had infringed on its patent portfolio. As such, the media characterized NTP as a species of patent troll.

Asserting patents as a business model is nothing new. In fact, a struggling Texas Instruments famously survived the 1980s by setting its legal department on every patent violator it could find (briefly making the legal department the company's largest profit center), which bought the company enough time for it to change its product emphasis from analog to digital and turn the company's fortunes around.

Some consider this a form of "patent trolling," a term that dates back to an early 1990s educational film on patents, which showed a green troll refusing passage over a bridge until each traveler paid a fee. Since then, however, although the term has entered everyday language, its precise definition has remained both elusive and controversial. Katharine Ku, the executive director of Stanford University's Office of Technology Licensing fully admits that her organization is acting as a non-practicing entity. As a manner of practice, however, Stanford does not engage in patent lawsuits, but rather licenses its technology to ventures that wish to commercialize the technology to build commercially successful businesses and further benefit society. Is Stanford a troll? IBM, the largest patent filer on the planet, has generated billions of dollars from patent licensing, often from IP that it has not commercialized itself. Is IBM a patent troll? Intellectual Ventures (IV), a patent assertion entity, has aggregated thousands of patents into portfolios, many of which were acquired from inventors who otherwise would not have been able to obtain any reward for their valuable innovations. IV does engage in legal assertions, but does so with solid arguments of infringement by the defending party. Is IV a patent troll?

Where there does seem to be agreement on the application of the term "troll" is when the non-practicing entity is broadly sending demand letters out with little or no evidence of infringement in hopes of obtaining a quick settlement. In October of 2016 the Federal Trade Commission released the results of a six-year study on this market behavior. The study kindly referred to these organizations as "Litigation PAEs." While in the study this type of organization only represented 20 percent of the total dollars associated with the patent licenses or settlements, they represented over 90 percent of the lawsuits.

There are many variations of patent licensing efforts with many associated labels: patent troll, patent pirate, patent shark, non-practicing entity, patent assertion entity and non-manufacturing patentee. Generally and simply, these are all forms of entities that exist primarily to use their patent holdings to leverage licensing revenues out of corporate targets. Some licensing activities involve valuable patents that are targeted at corporations that are interested in the use of the IP for a new business venture. Other licensing activities are targeted at existing infringers whose assertions are backed by solid research that demonstrates the infringement of the claims. However, many of these entities simply send assertion letters in an attempt to leverage the fact that it costs much more to defend a patent case than to prosecute one. In this case, the calculus involved is in pricing the license such that the target defendant concludes that it's far cheaper and less risky to just pay the ransom and be done with it.

How much money do patent trolls extract from America's businesses? The reports vary widely, from a couple billion dollars to $29 billion, according to a 2011 study conducted by the BBC. In addition, CNN has reported that researchers at the Santa Clara University School of Law found that 61 percent of all patent lawsuits in 2012 were brought by "trolls". And according to the website Ars Technica, by 2013, patent trolling had expanded from simply targeting the very largest corporations to attacking businesses on Main Street as well, with trolls suing more than three thousand firms with a median revenue of just $10 million.

Non-Practicing Entity (NPE) Lawsuits

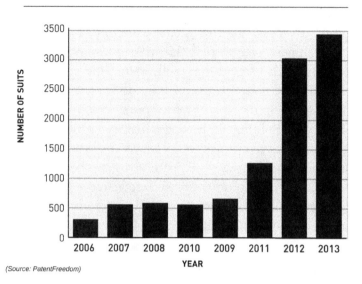

(Source: PatentFreedom)

The number of lawsuits initiated by Non-Practicing Entities (NPEs) has risen dramatically in recent years, impacting businesses of every size.

Patent Litgation Costs in the U.S.

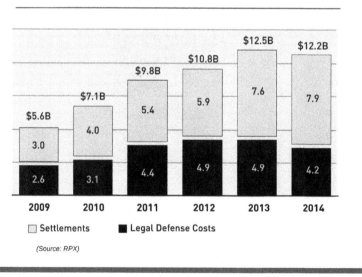

(Source: RPX)

Patent litigation costs in the US are on the rise, which can likely be attributed to increased NPE and troll-initiated lawsuits.

A 2014 Harvard University study also found that patent trolls were having a measurable and damaging impact on US competitiveness, with firms that were forced to pay trolls spending an average of $211 million less in R&D investments. It also found that trolls focused in particular on companies with large amounts of cash on hand. That finding might help to explain why Apple, which had one of the largest cash holdings in business history ($300 billion at one point), was the subject of 171 lawsuits brought by non-practicing entities—i.e., patent trolls—between 2009 and 2013. This problem wasn't exclusive to Apple; other notable troll targets were giant cash-rich innovators such as Hewlett-Packard, Samsung, AT&T and Dell.

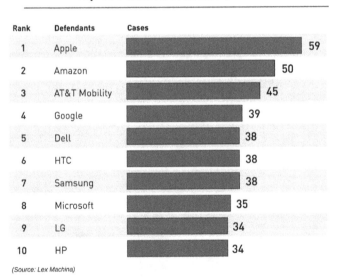

Top 10 Patent Defendants in 2013

Rank	Defendants	Cases
1	Apple	59
2	Amazon	50
3	AT&T Mobility	45
4	Google	39
5	Dell	38
6	HTC	38
7	Samsung	38
8	Microsoft	35
9	LG	34
10	HP	34

(Source: Lex Machina)

Many of the top patent lawsuit defendants are giant, cash-rich innovators – prime targets for trolls.

Perhaps most devastating of all was the discovery, announced in a July 2014 Price Waterhouse study, that patent trolls accounted for two-thirds of all patent lawsuits filed, up from 28 percent five years earlier.[1]   And, most recently, the 2016 FTC report showing that the vast majority of patent litigation cases are generated by trolls. Clearly, the trolls are multiplying.

But as frightening as these statistics may be, they pale in the face of the actual experience of a company embroiled in a patent fight. Which brings us back to the RIM case. It is a crazy and convoluted story, so we'll just focus on the high (or, rather, low) points.

RIM wasn't the only telecom company targeted by NTP. Other companies under attack, most notably Nokia and Good Technologies, quickly signed licensing deals. RIM, however, made a fatal decision to fight.

RIM's trial was set for the U.S. District Court for the Eastern District of Virginia, a court famous for being a "rocket docket," i.e., one that disposed of patent cases quickly. RIM's case rested on the fact that wireless email was already in the public domain before NTP was awarded its patent, thus rendering those patents invalid. That argument might have worked—had NTP's attorneys not discovered that RIM was using a version of software that was designed after NTP's patent had been granted. The jury found for NTP and ordered RIM to pay $33 million for past damages, an amount the judge bumped up to $53 million, not including the $4.5 million in legal fees it was required to pay NTP. Things only got worse from there. The judge also ordered that RIM cease and desist infringing upon those patents, effectively shutting down its network and business.

The court's decision had the potential to kill RIM. The company quickly appealed, however, and earned a stay on the injunction. Nonetheless, widespread publicity around the case devastated the company's stock price and eroded customer confidence.

Desperate, RIM representatives tried to negotiate a settlement with NTP, reportedly offering to pay $450 million. But negotiations collapsed, and the case went back to the courts. It was now 2005, five years after RIM had first been served. During those intervening years, a time when it was imperative that RIM executives focus on the bursting dot-com bubble and new competition on the smartphone front, the company leadership was distracted by the NTP case.

As a result of massive uncertainty around the service (in addition to the company being distracted from its core business), RIM's customers were also left hurting.

Then, in early 2006, RIM announced it had devised a number of software workarounds that enabled it to avoid infringing on NTP's patents. That announcement, however, only earned RIM a judicial rebuke. Citibank and other financial institutions managing RIM's shareholder interests, disgusted and outraged by management's IP business judgment, stepped in. Realizing RIM was out of options and needing to stop the bleeding for the sake of shareholders, they pressured the company to settle with NTP for $612.5 million.

The case was over but history had already passed RIM by. It would never again be a major player in the telecom business. Had RIM been able to invest that $600 million settlement fee in R&D, the company might have been able to advance the BlackBerry's design, thereby enabling it to become a contender in the emerging smartphone industry. Instead, the company has faded into near-oblivion.

There are a lot of lessons to take away from the RIM-NTP case, but perhaps the most important is that patent lawsuits can come at any time and from any source. In RIM's case, the attack arrived at the zenith of the company's success, from an opponent that RIM considered irrelevant. Because it saw NTP as little more than a nuisance and the case as absurd, RIM assumed eventual victory—a poorly informed, arrogant and cavalier executive action in the very serious world of patent litigation.

All in the Family

Again, when it comes to patent litigation, attacks on your IP can come from any direction— even from suppliers and customers.

Take Apple Inc. v. Samsung Electronics Co. In early January 2007, just days before Apple was to introduce the iPhone, the company filed four clusters of patents. That June, the company filed another set of patents covering nearly two hundred aspects of the iPhone's user interface.

Fast forward four years. In April 2011, Apple sued its own component supplier, Korean electronics giant Samsung, over claims that the latter had infringed upon those patents. The case was filed in the U.S. District Court for the Northern District of California—a location no doubt chosen, at least in part, because of a perception that the court favored important corporations within its jurisdiction.

What happened in the intervening years to explain Apple's move? In short: Android. An open smartphone platform designed to compete directly with Apple, Android was promulgated by Google and adopted by (among others) Samsung for its Galaxy phones. So Samsung was now not only a supplier to Apple, but also a competitive threat.

Samsung countersued Apple a week later, claiming that Apple had infringed on several of its core mobile-communications patents. In a likely attempt to capitalize on perceived international resentment of the US company's global dominance, Samsung filed its suits in Seoul, Tokyo and Mannheim, Germany.

And so the battle was joined. But what made this case particularly significant was its sheer scale: two of the wealthiest companies on the planet—that together had sold more than half of the world's smartphones—employing hundreds of attorneys to skirmish internationally over hundreds of points of dispute. At one point in 2012, Apple and Samsung were engaged in more than fifty cases in nine countries that totaled billions of dollars in potential damages. Both companies were at risk of not only losing a fortune, but also facing regional bans on the sales of their products. A US judge described one of the cases he was adjudicating as "one action in a worldwide constellation of litigation between the two companies."[2]

In the end, after three years of court battles across multiple nations, the result can only be described as a wash. Some courts found that Apple had violated Samsung's core patents; even more found that Samsung had violated Apple's. In addition, most requests for injunctions on sales were denied. And in the US, Samsung was ordered to pay approximately $200 million to Apple—an amount that probably didn't even cover the company's legal costs. Apple's victory in the case was, at best, pyrrhic.

That said, the lawsuits likely stalled Samsung, if only briefly, and created doubt in the minds of Samsung's potential customers—all just as the Android platform was beginning to take off.

As this case shows, even a company as powerful as Apple—or in similar cases, Texas Instruments, Motorola and even mighty IBM—can pull out its patent arsenal in an IP battle and play hardball. Indeed, any company that finds itself facing hard times—declining revenues, profits or market share, or some combination of thereof— may find itself adopting a strategy of digging through its active patent files looking for justification to sue any target it can find. And not just competitors but—as we've just seen—even suppliers, partners and customers.

A Matter of Timing

Both Congress and the White House have struggled mightily over the last decade to deal with the numerous threats posed by patent trolls. But the government has had to move gingerly, because as much as it seeks to protect the economy from opportunistic parties shaking down and extorting companies big and small, it also needs to ensure that worthy challengers to patent holders get their day in court and aren't crushed by giant enterprises backed by armies of attorneys.

In September 2011, Congress passed the America Invents Act (AIA), which is also known as the Leahy-Smith Act in honor of its lead sponsors. The AIA switched the U.S. Patent Office process from a "first-to-invent" to a "first-inventor-to-file" system in order to be more congruent with patent laws in other major countries. Though generally hailed as an improvement, one of the unforeseen consequences of the AIA has been that it makes it even easier for patent challengers to revisit the validity of issued patents. While the AIA deters some patent holders from trotting their patents into litigation for fear of having one of their crown jewels killed in a post-grant examination, a new kind of troll has figured out how to use the threat of invalidity as a weapon against the patent holder itself.

This second consequence of the AIA was the creation of the Patent Trial & Appeals Board (PTAB), a new administrative body within the patent office that decides issues of patentability. The PTAB is made up of two divisions. The Appeals Division, which is composed of more than a hundred patent judges, handles appeals of patent examiner rejections. More important for our purposes, however, is the Trial Division, which handles contested patent cases. Among its most notable procedures is the inter partes review (IPR), which is used to challenge the legitimacy of one or more claims in a US patent, and even the validity of the patent itself.[3] An IPR is effectively a re-examination of the patent, but with a whole lot more scrutiny and subject to the most recent set of rules (e.g., the Supreme Court ruling in Alice)

What on first glance might appear as a safeguard for existing patent holders has proven to be just the opposite, a vulnerability made clear in the case of Kyle Bass, a hedge fund manager and the founder and principal of the Dallas-based Hayman Capital Management, LP. Bass first made his name in 2008 after purchasing credit default swaps (the equivalent to "shorting" stocks) on the subprime securities issued by a number of investment firms, thereby becoming one of the few winners in the Great Recession of that year.

On the heels of this financial success, Bass teamed up with Erich Spangenberg (widely known as "the world's most notorious patent troll"[4]) and founded a pharmaceutical company called the Coalition for Affordable Drugs. The company's express goal was to use inter partes review to challenge pharmaceutical patents. Frequently, a small set of pharmaceutical patents represents a sizable, concentrated chunk of a company's revenue and earnings. By August 2015 Bass and Spangenberg had filed eighteen petitions against such patents—but only after Bass had shorted the targeted companies. By crashing their stock prices, Bass was thus able to make a quick and sizable profit. In his own words, he "knee-capped" the drug companies.

After being labeled a patent troll, Bass responded that he was merely trying to encourage competition among pharmaceutical companies and thus bring down the cost of medicine. He later admitted that he was indeed only after the money, at one point stating that "At the heart of nearly every patent...the motivation is profit." In fact, Bass justified his actions by saying he wasn't alone in his actions, and that his targets, notably Celgene Corp., were greedy too, said Bass.

Bass' actions were an unintended consequence of the AIA. Two years later, President Obama announced several executive orders tightening the transparency of, and scrutiny over, broad patent claims, noting that his orders were designed "to protect innovators from frivolous litigation" by patent trolls.[5]

Over time, we believe the narrowing of vague and overly broad claims will have a positive effect. For the last few decades the focus of patent drafting and prosecution has been to obtain a granted patent and, ideally, a patent that can create leverage for uses never intended or even imagined. It was a numbers game, like buying a bag of collectors' stamps in the hope that there would be something of value inside. If the patents protecting your revenue streams are solid, then Kyle Bass and his imitators are not a threat.

But what of your company-defining patents? Are they at risk? What percent of your portfolio can survive an IPR challenge? It's likely that you are far more vulnerable than you think.

Shareholder Revolt

We still aren't finished with this nightmare scenario, however, because what is particularly worrying here is that patent trolls have proven to be as adaptive as the companies trying to defend themselves against them.

The newest wrinkle in patent trolling is the patent activist shareholder. If you picked up this book because your company neither knows nor cares much about its IP portfolio, this is the trend you should worry about most. Patent activist shareholders don't concern themselves with buying up patents and then suing companies for infringement. Rather, they only need to buy a few shares in a company, then sue it for a failure to make best use of the IP under its control or for misreporting the strength and value of its IP position.

This, in fact, could be your worst nightmare.

The only good news is that the age of patent activist shareholders is taking longer to arrive than expected, probably because shareholders are still as ignorant about IP as company executives. But make no mistake: patent activist shareholders are coming. A fair warning came in 2012, when a group called Starboard Value attacked the board of AOL over a lack of IP strategy, forcing AOL management to sell a significant portion of its strategic patent assets to Microsoft. Starboard then went after chipmaker MIPS Technologies and forced it to sell a massive part of its valuable portfolio to Bridge Crossing.[6] One-time revenue opportunities spike short-term shareholder value, but can have a devastating effect on management's ability to control its destiny.

Before we go any further, here are some questions that require your attention:

- Is an outsized portion of your revenue protected by a small set of patents?
- Have your competitors surrounded your IP position, making it difficult to freely operate within major product lines?
- Are you prepared to sell off your patent holdings? Your key patents? Do you even know what they are?

- Given this enormous potential vulnerability, how much of your business is protected by just a few key patents—or even just one—that your company cannot afford to lose and still keep your business alive?

Unless you are able to answer these questions, patent trolls, desperate competitors and patent activist shareholders will soon enough answer them for you.

In the long term, the shift away from operational barriers combined with the "great global patent war" will surely pose a threat to your company. You know you must strategize and plan for the future. But you face a more immediate challenge. Right now, in fact. You need to understand the contents of your patent portfolio—and you must constantly attend to it. You need to understand the patents held by those who might pose a threat to you—and you must constantly monitor them. Many people mistakenly think they're set once they have what they believe to be a solid IP strategy and patent portfolio.

They are wrong. The truth is that IP portfolios, just like investment portfolios, are subject to many changing conditions. Rules are made and amended, competitors progress, markets ebb and flow, and patents grow old and lose their potency as competing patents surround and supersede them. Patent experts have a term for this: patent rot. It's as though your patent portfolio is aging. As a result, you must work to keep it vital and healthy. If you leave it alone, it will wither and become vulnerable to external agents, including patent trolls.

Trolls and other sources of litigation are scary, and the new types of trolls are even scarier than traditional ones. But you can protect your company from these bad actors—and in the process gain an advantage over your competitors. We'll show you how to do this later in the book. For now, it is enough that you appreciate that this threat is current and real, and that you prepare yourself to take the actions necessary to repel it.

_____

Part II Introduction

In Part I, we showed you the threat. In Part III we will show you how to respond to that threat.

But before we can do that, we must first make sure that you have a baseline knowledge about the world of patents and trade secrets. We are living in a new "post-operational" competitive era. Before your company can thrive within it (and we will get to that), you must first learn how you're going to survive.

The first thing to understand is that intellectual property has many similarities to physical property. That is, your relationship to physical property can take three forms:

- You can rent it
- You can own it
- You can exit it

It's really that simple. Much of what is true for physical property is true for IP. And just as with physical property rights, intellectual property rights are not something you can just ignore. Many companies have learned the hard way that you can't just use someone else's patented idea without having already reached some licensing agreement with that party. As with physical property, you may be able to squat on someone else's space for a while; eventually, however, there will be a painful reckoning in the form of an eviction or a lawsuit.

At the same time, you can't earn a patent and simply stick the paperwork in some forgotten filing cabinet. That's the IP equivalent of owning an abandoned lot: you not only lose any potential revenues from developing the property but you may also find that your neighbors have encroached on it so much that it no longer has any practical value.

This all may seem obvious. But you need only glance at today's business news to find at least one story of a company whose executives ignored their IP, or violated the IP of a competitor, and now find themselves hauled into court and embroiled in expensive litigation.

The core message of this book is that you will not be able to thrive in this new competitive era without a tight focus, to the point of obsession, on the creation, curation, quality and health of your IP portfolio. You must also have a willingness to change your corporate culture. But before you can do that, you must first understand what you don't know about IP.

For that reason, we suggest that your executive team, and most important, your CEO, take the following "IP-IQ" test. It's the best use you can make of the next fifteen minutes and it may just save your butt. (And the good news is that the only grade you get is the one you give yourself.)

The IP-IQ Test

1. List the top five determining factors in valuing your company's patent portfolio.
2. What is the value of your company's patent portfolio on your balance sheet?
3. What impact did the recent game-changing Supreme Court decisions —Alice, Mayo and Nautilus— have on your current patent portfolio? What effects have they had on your patent strategy?
4. Describe the idea-to-innovation-to-invention process at your company. How would you rank your company's IP strategy and process

effectiveness relative to your competition?

5. Leading corporations implement IP strategies that contribute hundreds of millions, even billions, of dollars directly to their annual EBITA and/ or balance sheets. How would you assess the annual financial impact of your IP strategy?

6. What impact has the America Invents Act of 2013 had on your company's product and innovation strategy?

7. What is your company's ratio of patent filings to research and development spending, and how does that ratio compare to your closest competitors?

8. What do the core patents filed by your top three competitors and the up-and-coming disruptive innovators in your industry reveal to you regarding their strategy?

9. What precautions have you taken to protect your company from shareholder lawsuits related to under-optimizing your company's IP assets and/or misrepresenting the dynamic value of the IP portfolio?

10. Who are the top inventors in your company? Can you describe the expertise of each of them? What are you doing to maximize the impact of their innovation and creativity on your company's performance?

11. When evaluating your leadership team, what percentage of how they are assessed is based upon their contribution to new innovations, inventions and/or patents?

12. On how many patents or trade secrets were you personally named as an inventor in the last year?

13. What return on investment (ROI) could you realize from your IP portfolio assets and how do you measure that? What is your actual current ROI on those assets?

14. What methodology do you use to hire inventors? What metrics do you use to reward your inventors? How do you recognize inventors in your company? Are these programs competitive in your industry?

15. What part does "open innovation"—that is, the acceptance of outside sources, from licensing to crowd-sourcing for innovation—play in your company's innovation/invention strategy?
16. Extra Credit: Explain the Patent Trial and Appeal Board's (PTAB) use of the patent inter partes review process. How is this process used by activist shareholders to attack corporations?

Feeling a bit dazed and confused? Don't worry—you're not alone. In fact, many CEOs we interviewed answered a lot of these questions with some variation of "I have a really smart person who has that information" or "That's for the lawyers to handle." And while these answers might have been acceptable as recently as a decade ago, they no longer are.

Today, if you think these matters should be left to your attorneys or IP specialist you are wrong—and dangerously so. Even if you are not directly involved in the actual IP process, you still must remain deeply engaged with that process. Why?

Because you cannot set a model and create a viable culture of invention if you remain an outsider to that very culture.

These days, the IP world is changing as fast as the digital world. If you were still using three-generation-old computers and microprocessors, you would be fired. Very soon the same will be true if knowledge of IP is equally limited—and rightly so.

The bad news is that no one was born knowing this stuff. The good news is that it is all learnable. In this section we will show you how to gain that knowledge, as well as how to put it to effective use.

For now, here are the things you need to know:

- The legal and business basics of IP
- How IP has historically related to corporate value creation
- How patents can function as a vitally important information and financial resource at your company

Once you understand these basics, we'll help you build upon this knowledge and, in turn, apply the advanced concepts of Inventioneering that will enable your company to thrive.

IP knowledge is not just for legal professionals anymore. There is no going back: You can no longer refuse to participate in the new world of IP competition. You can only go forward, and you must remain on the offense. But you cannot do that until you understand the weapons in your arsenal and how to put them to use.

In this chapter we'll give you an executive-level basic education in intellectual property, focused on patents, trade secrets and IP economics. Even if you have some experience in this field, we suggest you take the time to read it, as even IP veterans often have a hard time keeping up with the changes. In addition, patent law experts themselves often don't fully appreciate the economics of patents or the unique liabilities that IP places on corporate senior management—and especially upon boards of directors.

Chapter 5

Innovation is Insufficient

Ideas vs. Innovation vs. Invention

One of the biggest—and most dangerous—mistakes that enterprises make is to confuse the process of creation with its realization. Too many companies build a powerful engine of creativity and then fail to convert that creativity into real products and services that generate revenues and profits and capture market share. The R&D department buzzes away, regularly demonstrating clever new ideas to senior management, but too often those ideas don't end up in the company's product catalog. The result is that the lab becomes little more than a think tank, product development attends only to maintaining current products and services and, inexplicably to senior management and the board, the company slowly loses competitiveness and falls behind its competitors despite having a superior lineup of scientists and engineers in its lab.

Simply put, ideas aren't enough. They are merely a start. Those ideas must be converted into innovations. These innovations, if incremental, can become enhancements to existing products and services; if seminal, they become the basis of wholly new offerings.

But the process cannot end there, because innovations left in an unprotected state are vulnerable to theft by fast followers, and thus fail at their core purpose of maximizing revenues and profits to the company. They must be taken to the next step, which is invention. Invention is the formalization and protection of ideas and innovations. Specifically, invention brings ideas and innovations under the purview of the laws of intellectual property.

In the same way that individuals can secure the rights to physical property (by renting or buying real estate, for example), inventors can apply for and gain the rights to intellectual property that they invent or create. IP is defined as inventions or processes that derive from creative work of the mind. Inventors may be granted the exclusive rights to their intellectual property by federal law via several legal protection methods. However, not every method of IP protection is suitable for every invention. The invention itself will determine what method of protection is most appropriate.

With a focus on the utilitarian (as opposed to the artistic) and an emphasis on patents and trade secrets (as opposed to trademarks and copyrights), here is an overview of the important components of your company's intellectual property protection.

Patent Basics for the CEO

Let's begin with a few definitions.

What is intellectual property?

Recent years have seen the rise of a similar term, intellectual capital. The two are related but nonetheless distinctly different. Intellectual capital is basically the modern name for the traditional accounting term "intangible assets," factors that provide added value to a company in the form of goodwill, management talent, product quality, public reputation, etc. Although intellectual capital does not appear on the traditional balance sheet, it adds to the perceived value of the enterprise as a whole.

Consider Facebook, for example. The monetization potential inherent in the fact of the company's one billion users gives Facebook a market value many times that of its actual revenues. The same is true of Apple, which became the world's most valuable manufacturer not just because of its annual sales, but because its stock price reflected the market's belief that Apple would remain the world's leading innovator in consumer electronics.

There have been a number of attempts in the last three decades to find a way to empirically audit and record a company's intellectual capital assets, but to date no formal or complete system has emerged.

Intellectual property, on the other hand, is a bit better understood—it is defined in the rules of accounting and has a place on the balance sheet. That said, there is a growing recognition that intellectual property also has its own intellectual capital asset—that is, IP also creates certain intangible assets whose value is often overlooked. We mention this because one of the themes of this book is that intellectual property adds value to a company whose corporate culture is designed to develop its products and services in concert with all legal protections available.

For our purposes, IP is the total of all of the patents and trade secrets in your company's ownership. (For full accounting practices you would also include copyrights and trademarks.)

Patent Section Headers

TITLE: The title of the invention. "A Method for Manufacturing Widgets"

FIELD OF THE INVENTION (optional) The field that the invention relates to.

BACKGROUND: A generalized description of prior art.

SUMMARY: (optional): A sentence summarizing the invention, focusing on the most novel aspects.

BRIEF DESCRIPTION OF THE DRAWINGS: A description of what is contained in the drawings. "Figure 1 illustrates an embodiment of an X"

DETAILED DESCRIPTION: A description of the invention. "Figure 1 illustrates an embodiment of an X"

CLAIMS: The claims lay out the metes and bounds of what is protected by the patent. "A method of manufacturing widgets comprising..."

What is a patent?

In the United States, a patent is a twenty-year government-granted monopoly for an invention, which is a product or a process that provides, in general, a new way of doing something or offers a new technical solution to a problem. A patent does not directly give you the right to ship your product. Rather, a patent potentially allows you to stop someone else from shipping their product. If you have evidence that another company, without your agreement, is making, using or selling your invention in the same country that awarded your patent, you can then ask the courts to stop it from doing so.

A patent is constructed in three sections: the claims, the figures and the descriptions. The most important of the three sections is the claims. We say this for two reasons: First, the claims comprise the legal description of the invention, and therefore dictate the actual boundaries of your intellectual property ownership. The rest of the patent is simply there to support the claims. Second, most CEOs read a part of a patent description, such as the summary or abstract, and believe they understand the legally protected invention. Most often they do not. Summaries and abstracts can sound really good, much better than the inventive claims warrants, when in reality the summary and abstract may not accurately convey what is protected.

What makes an invention patentable?

At the most basic level, an invention must fulfill the following requirements to be considered for a patent:

1. The subject matter must be patent-eligible. Section 101 of the U.S. Patent Act, found in Title 35 of the United States Code, states that "Whoever invents or discovers any new and useful process, machine, manufacture, or composition of matter, or any new and useful improvement thereof, may obtain a patent therefor, subject to the conditions and requirements of this title."

Things that are not patentable include:

a. Laws of nature: You cannot, for example, patent nuclear fusion, gravity, electron spin or cloning
b. Physical phenomena or products of nature: Naturally occurring chemical compounds, wildlife or plants cannot be patented.
c. Abstract ideas such as concepts, formulas or algorithms: This one is tricky, as the boundaries between algorithms and software programs aren't clear. According to Ken LaMance, an attorney at LegalMatch: "Although software functions by using algorithms and mathematics, it may be patentable if it produces some concrete and useful result. However, what cannot be patented is software whose only purpose is to perform mathematical operations. Thus, software that converts one set of numbers to another will not be patentable, but software that converts one set of numbers to another to make rubber will be patentable."

d. Artistic works: Music, literature and art
    may not be patented; they may, however,
    be eligible for copyright protection

Simply stated, discoveries within the natural world
cannot be patented, having existed prior to being
discovered. However, inventions utilizing discoveries,
or applications of such discoveries, can be patented.

2. The invention must be new or novel. If an invention
    was known to the public prior to an inventor filing a
    patent application, the invention cannot be considered
    new or novel, and is therefore not patentable. In other
    words, a patent cannot be granted if it prevents people
    from doing what they had previously been free to
    do. This requirement for novelty exists to ensure that
    existing inventions, also known as prior art (discussed
    in greater detail below), are not patented again. All
    information relevant to a patent's claims of novelty that
    has been disclosed to the public, no matter the form
    in which it was presented, is considered prior art.

3. An invention must be non-obvious. This means that
    an invention must be a non-obvious improvement
    over existing products or practices. If it is deemed that
    an invention could easily be discovered by someone
    of "ordinary knowledge" or follow from "normal
    development" in a given field, the invention is not
    patentable. Additionally, If the invention is simply
    a routine or predictable combination or application
    of existing technology, it is not patentable.

4. An invention must be useful, meaning that the
    USPTO's patent examiners must determine
    that an invention has a specific utility.

What exactly is prior art?

There are two forms of prior art. The first form (35 U.S.C. 102) occurs when a person or company applies for a patent for an invention believed to be new, only to find that it is not. The second form (35 U.S.C. 103) is known as an "obvious" invention—that is, when two or more previously introduced products or publicly documented inventions are combined. Both forms of prior art result in an invention being denied a patent.

What is "First to File"?

The subject of who actually deserves a patent is the stuff of both entertaining myth and history—think of Thomas Edison and Alexander Graham Bell and other races to the patent office—but when it is your patent application on the line, first to file becomes deadly serious.

This is where the Leahy-Smith/America Invents Act, which we discussed in the previous chapter, comes into play. It defines who has the right to patent an invention. Whereas the US had previously operated under a "first-to-invent" system, AIA resulted in patent law being changed to a "first-inventor-to-file" system. The bill represented the most significant amendment to the American patent system in recent history—and perhaps ever. In any case, any patents filed prior to March 16, 2013 (or claiming priority to a patent application filed before that date), are subject to laws of the previous system, in which a patent is granted to the first person to "reduce the invention to practice," or bring it to reality.

Effective March 16, 2013, however, the patent rights to a given invention now belong to the first person to file a patent application on that invention, regardless of who the first inventor may be, the date of the invention's conception or evidence of reduction to practice. You might hear of nuances regarding the AIA, but the bottom line is this: If you believe you have a patentable invention, it is in your best interest to file a patent as soon as possible. AIA represents a major shift in US patent law, but it also brings that law more in alignment with international patent law, since most countries have adhered to a philosophy of first-to-file for generations.

What Makes Someone an Inventor?

Anyone who contributes to even one part of one claim that is granted is required to be listed as an inventor on that patent. All inventors are joint owners of the entire patent unless otherwise assigned to another party. Failure to list an inventor on a patent or listing someone who is not an inventor on a patent is grounds for invalidating the entire patent.

Who owns a patent?

As an officer, you probably want your company to own all patents. According to US patent law, however, inventors are entitled to joint ownership of a patent unless they assign their patent rights to another person or entity. Most companies require new employees and contractors to sign an agreement that grants the company full ownership of any relevant invention. However, it is also a good practice to have inventors sign an assignment agreement designating the corporate entity the assignee for each and every invention. It would be highly risky for a company to rely solely on a generic employment agreement to establish ownership of a particular patent right.

How do you obtain a US patent?

The United States Patent and Trademark Office (USPTO) is a federal government agency responsible for the processing of US patent applications. Typically, a patent attorney or patent agent drafts a US patent application (claims, figures, description) on behalf of your company. Once an application is submitted to the USPTO, patent hopefuls are likely to face a waiting period of between six months and three years before their application is up for review. Once it is, one of the office's approximately eight thousand US patent examiners will test the application for "patentability," "novelty" and "non-obviousness"—any one of which can result in one or more rejections against a patent claim. It usually takes three or four negotiating rounds with an examiner before a final disposition is reached, so you'll need to resign yourself to the likelihood of a prolonged negotiation with a government agency. (Fun, right?) The examination period has been known to take even longer but you do have the option of paying a fee to accelerate the process (think FedEx for patents).

Patent Filing Process

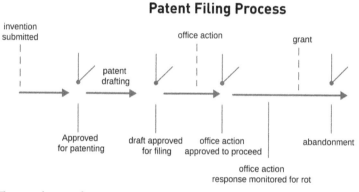

The typical process for a U.S. patent takes 3-4 years and requires 3 exchanges with the USPTO.

How does my company obtain patent protection in other countries?

There are over one hundred and thirty countries where patent rights can be obtained. Typically, you have a one-year grace period after filing in the United States before having to file in non-US jurisdictions. However, most countries that issue patents participate in what is known as the Patent Cooperation Treaty (PCT), which allows you to file your patent application with one organization within in the grace period, and preserves your right to file in other countries for another eighteen months after that. But be warned: foreign filing and the associated legal and governmental fees can become exorbitant.

Obtaining & Mainting Patents
on a *Single* Invention in the 50+
Major Countries of the World
Costs More than...

US $500,000

over the 20-year life of the patent.

What is a trade secret?

According to John P. Hutchins, author of "The
Corporation's Valuable IP Assets: IP Rights Under SOX
[Sarbanes-Oxley]," an article that appeared in a course
handbook published by the Practicing Law Institute,
US companies own more than $5 trillion in trade secret
information. Unlike a patent, a trade secret requires no
registration and has no expiration date. (One of the world's
most famous trade secrets is the formula for making Coca-
Cola, which has remained a tightly held secret for more
than a hundred and twenty-five years.) To qualify as a
trade secret the invention must conform to three rules:
it cannot be generally known to the public, it must have
economic value derived from being kept secret and the
company must make efforts to maintain the secrecy of the
invention. The most straightforward way to create a trade
secret is to draft a patent application but not file it with the
USPTO. Instead, mark the application "Confidential/Trade
Secret" and then protect and monitor access to it. Just as
your employees and contractors sign IP assignment rights
transfer agreements for relevant inventions, those who have
access to trade secrets should acknowledge the importance
and confidentiality of the company's trade secrets.

Congratulations! You've just completed a course in Basic Patent Law: Rules and Definitions. Not as painful as you thought, is it? No doubt you already knew much of this, but it's also likely there were some holes in your knowledge base that we've been able to fill.

And since we are all now on the same page in our understanding of patent basics, we can move on to see how patents and trade secrets impact the daily operations, long-term strategy and revenues of your company. We'll also look closely at the real-life cost of obtaining a valuable IP portfolio.

Don't hesitate to refer back to this chapter.

We do it all the time.

In this chapter, we'll take a detailed look at what it takes, both in terms of process and costs, to develop and maintain a corporate patent portfolio. You may be surprised not only by the complexity of the process and its expenses, but also by the high level of commitment to that process by some well-known corporations.

Chapter 6

Patent Economics for the CEO

P atents have become and will continue to be a major practice for many of the world's most powerful companies. Here is a list of the corporations that earned the largest number of patents from the USPTO in 2014.

Top Patenting Companies
(US Granted - 2014)

Rank	Company Name	Patents Earned	
1	IBM	7481	(Source: www.IPO.org)
2	Samsung	4936	
3	Canon	4172	
4	Sony	3214	
5	Microsoft	2983	
6	Google	2881	
7	Toshiba	2850	
8	Qualcomm	2706	
9	Panasonic	2394	
10	General Electrics	2293	
11	LG Electronics	2119	
12	Hitachi	2030	
13	Apple	2003	
14	Intel	1965	
15	AT&T	1896	
16	Fujitsu	1812	
17	Medtronics	1716	
18	Seiko Epson	1660	
19	Ricoh	1634	
20	Hewlett-Packard	1631	

This table ranks the corporations that earned the largest number of patents from the USPTO in 2014.

This chart should give you a sense of how your company compares to the world's most prolific patent filers. Even just glancing at this table, you'll notice that these companies are long-standing leading innovators and highly valued companies in their technological areas. That's not a coincidence.

But the sheer number of patents is only the start. To this first table we now add the amount each company spends on research and development. Divide this number by the company's total patents and you get an idea of how much each is willing to spend to earn a new patent. It also offers a clue to their "innovative efficiency." Beware, however, because the final number is also influenced by how active each of these companies is in filing new patents.

This table shows the annual amount each company spent on research and development, divided by the company's patent grants for that year. This metric can be used as a IP budgeting guideline.

Research & Development Spend per Patent
(SAMPLING, 2014)

Company Name	Patents	R&D Spend ($Billions)	~R&D Spend/Patent ($Millions)
IBM	7481	6.2	0.8
Samsung	4396	13.4	2.7
Microsoft	2983	10.4	3.5
Google	2881	8.0	2.8
Apple	2003	6.0	3.0
Intel	1965	10.6	5.4
General Motors	1470	7.2	4.9
Cisco	1127	5.9	5.2
Honda	1099	6.3	5.7
Amazon	741	6.6	8.9
Roche	484	10.0	20.7
Facebook	279	1.1	4.0

(Source: www.IPO.org)

Note that this table represents only new, originally created patents by those companies, and does not account for patents purchased, acquired through M&A or licensed (as distinct from those earned through application). In some years, companies such as Google and Apple spent more on purchasing, acquiring and licensing patents than they did on all R&D. During those years they showed a common pattern of acquiring companies in order to build their patent portfolios.

Keep in mind that what we have illustrated so far is the amount of research and development money these well-known companies spend to generate an innovation they believe is worth pursuing as a legally protected invention. But this, of course, is only the first step. The application to protect the invention must also be filed, prosecuted and maintained over a twenty-year lifespan. What we're describing is a time-consuming and expensive process, costing an average of $60,000 for a US patent. Here's how it breaks out:

Large Corp US Patent Cost: ~60k per Active Asset
(Avg Complexity - Non-Accelerated)

1) Application Creation	
a. Search	$2,000
b. Legal Drafting	$11,000
c. Gov & Admin	$2,000
	$15,000
2) Application Prosecution (Avg 3 Office Actions)	
a. Legal Prosecution	$10,000
b. Extended Prosecution	$3,000
c. Gov Allowance and Admin	$2,000
	$15,000
3) Post Grant Maintenance	
a. Gov Fees and Admin	**$13,000**
4) Non-Allowed or Abandoned Apportionment	**$7,000**
5) Inventor and Management Overhead	**$10,000**
Total	**$60,000**

(Source: The American Intellectual Property Lawyers Association, Bi-Annual Survey 2015)

Let's look at that chart more closely.

Application Creation: What you cannot see is that there have been significant changes in this process over the last decade as many corporations have demanded that the patent industry move from a billable-hour fee structure to a fixed- or capped-fee structure. An estimated half of all patents filed today by large corporations are handled with a fixed-fee or capped-fee arrangement.

This new arrangement usually features three levels of patent complexity and associated pricing. Thus, low-complexity patent applications might cost $8,000 to draft, medium complexity applications $10,000 and high complexity applications more than $12,000. (In line 1b., we use $11,000 as a weighted average). Fixed-fee terms are increasingly being applied to all aspects of the legal service component of the patent process. As a result, legal service providers have been hard-pressed to maintain the margins they previously enjoyed under the billable-hour approach. An unintended consequence is that patent quality has suffered as a result.

Application Prosecution: We estimate three office actions as the average for a company to reach final resolution of a given patent application. However, in many instances, extended prosecution (2b) occurs, in which case the corporation chooses to prosecute patents beyond the standard range (e.g., request for appeal or request for continued examination).

Post-Grant Maintenance: All patents are subject to maintenance fees to keep the patent active. The total for large corporations—the four-, eight- and twelve-year marks—is currently about $13,000 from the point of grant to patent expiration. Failure to pay maintenance fees results in the forfeiture of the company's rights to that patent.

Non-Allowed or Abandoned Apportionment: Approximately 50 percent of all US patent applications are granted. As this ratio includes individual inventors and small companies, which abandon the patent application process at a much higher rate, it's clear that large corporations enjoy a higher grant rate than average (which is why we used a 75 percent allowance rate in line 4 of the table). Corporations simply have better and more professional internal processes, as well as greater monetary and human resources to follow through to the end.

That said, even large corporations are prudent enough to abandon some of their applications. In fact, as you can see, they should probably do so more often. (The amortized cost for patent applications filed and prosecuted but not granted is covered in line 4.)

Inventor & Management Overhead: This includes internal management of the invention process, a small allocation for inventor time and management of external counsel, including for the patent application review process.

This chart shows costs for a non-accelerated patent application. However, an increasing number of companies are beginning to use what is known as the Track One accelerated process, which requires a response from the USPTO within one year and final resolution within eighteen months. Track One costs large corporations $4,000 per patent application, but we've found (as have others who have analyzed the process) that the total cost can be the same or even less than for non-accelerated applications, and that the grant rate is consistently higher.

Next, here's a quick look at how these costs shake out in terms of where the money is spent:

Patent Cost Breakdown

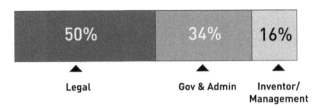

One third of patent costs are fixed governmental expenses.

"Legal" refers to all attorney fees, including outside counsel for the drafting of the application and prosecution phase with a USPTO examiner. There are typically three examinations per patent application, but it's not uncommon for examinations to go well beyond that number. For example, our worst-case scenario patent went through eleven rounds of examination, continued examinations and appeals before ultimately being awarded a grant.

After two or three examinations, an appeal process is mandated, which requires escalation within the USPTO process—not to mention additional attorney and USPTO fees (which are covered in line 2b of the "Large Corp. Patent Cost" table above).

"Government & Administrative" fees are hard costs that are non-negotiable requirements. Think of them as a government tax.

"Inventor/Management" fees are probably underrepresented in this chart. Large corporations tend to employ one in-house patent manager (often a non-practicing patent attorney) per every fifty to one hundred and fifty applications filed annually. Typically, these inside patent managers also have a manager above them, and at least one administrative employee they oversee. The inventor time-cost in particular is often much greater than represented in these numbers. In good corporate culture, invention should be considered an important part of the job.

Finally, a quick look at international patent filing. Here's a simple timeline of the process (note: not to scale) to give you a sense of how long a global patent filing typically takes:

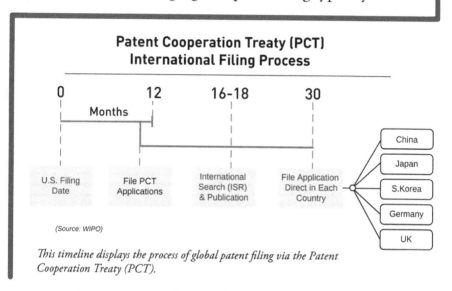

**Patent Cooperation Treaty (PCT)
International Filing Process**

This timeline displays the process of global patent filing via the Patent Cooperation Treaty (PCT).

The bottom line is that you have basically twelve months after filing for patent protection in the United States to file under the Patent Cooperation Treaty (PCT), which preserves your right to file in any of the 148 countries participating in the PCT.

The cost of filing in the different countries varies. Here is a list of the most important jurisdictions among the countries, which represent about 80 percent of all patent applications and grants worldwide.

International Patent Costs

Jurisdiction	Cost in US Dollars
+Patent Cooperation Treaty (PCT)	$2,500
China	$25,000
Japan	$25,000
S. Korea	$25,000
Germany	$20,000
UK	$7,500
Total	**$105,000**

(Source: www.WIPO.int)

The table shows filing costs in the most important jurisdictions outside of the US. Patents filed in these countries, along with those filed in the US, represent about 80 percent of all patent applications and grants worldwide.

As you can see, it's important to select which patents and which countries are most important to your business because, as the table shows, it costs approximately $100,000 to file and maintain a single patent in just those five jurisdictions, and it would cost about $500,000 to file and maintain a single patent in all 148 countries participating in the PCT. For example, Amazon files very few patent applications outside of the US, and one benefit of not filing internationally is that the company can keep its patent applications secret from the public until they are granted. If your company intends to file for international coverage through the PCT, the patent application must be published by the USPTO, which happens about a year and a half after the filing.

This final chart shows that it can sometimes be a better strategy to invest in buying patents as opposed to creating them internally. This is especially true when you are looking for patents for defensive purposes such as competitive encircling strategies.

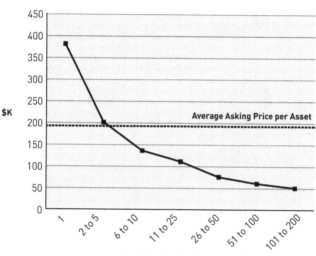

Per-Asset Asking Price by Portfolio Size

$K

Average Asking Price per Asset

Portfolio Size (number of assets)

This chart gives the reader a sense of the market asking price per patent and how the per patent price declines when bought as a portfolio.

The horizontal axis represents the number of assets (pending patents as well as granted patents) in a sale. The message here is that the average portfolio value on the open market is about $50,000 per asset, when purchased in quantity. (By comparison, if a company cherry-picks and only buys the most valuable patent, the average price is around $400,000 per patent.) Thus, as you can see, acquiring patents is a cost-competitive method of building a patent portfolio. As a result, many large corporations have adopted a two-pronged approach for their IP strategy: improving competitive advantage by creating their own patents and enhancing their portfolio by buying others.

We have now looked at the entire patent process, starting with basic rules and concluding with implementation within an organization. But one final step—perhaps the most important one—still remains: how to turn new ideas not just into intellectual property but to take them beyond IP—into actual innovations, products and revenues, and profits. This is where the IP rubber hits the road; go no further and you will be just another company with a file cabinet stuffed with patents that were never put to use.

In upcoming chapters, we're going to show you how to turn that paper into gold.

Earlier in the book we touched on the difference between innovation and invention. In this chapter we will explore both more deeply, and in the process show how and why corporate value accretion in the twenty-first century has begun to shift from the first to the second.

Chapter 7

Invention and Value Creation: A History

The goal of all societies throughout human history has been to become wealthier. But it was not until the eighteenth century that there was a structured way to grow wealth—that is, to increase economic power rather than simply expand a society's material holdings.

It was during the First Industrial Revolution, beginning in 1760, that the world saw the greatest explosion of the business application of new ideas, including those from Newton, Descartes, Leibniz, Boyle and Darwin.

During that era, human history underwent a profound shift, one as great as the rise of agriculture five millennia before. Now, for the first time, it was possible to create wealth through new ideas, rather than resorting to war in order to steal riches from one's neighbors. Not only was it possible to bring large numbers of investigators to bear on a single challenge—such as an epidemic or faster travel—but the results of individual research could be more easily shared and added to an ever-growing body of knowledge. The result was the widespread increase in the quality of human life as measured by GDP.

Consider the chart below:

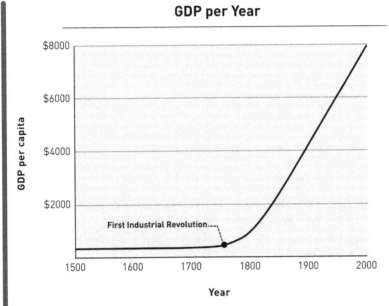

GDP per Year

After the first Industrial Revolution, it is evident that the GDP growth trend increased dramatically.

Suddenly, wealth had a new definition. In the words of veteran entrepreneur and executive Nick Hanauer and economic historian Eric Beihnocker:

"Prosperity in a society is the accumulation of solutions to human problems...Ultimately, the measure of a society's wealth is the range of human problems that it has found a way to solve and how available it has made those solutions to its citizens. Every item in the huge retail stores that Americans shop in can be thought of as a solution to a different kind of problem—how to eat, clothe ourselves, make our homes more comfortable, get around, entertain ourselves, and so on. The more and better solutions available to us, the more prosperity we have."[7]

For companies, this meant a continuous race against competitors to achieve three things:

1. 1.New product creation (new product, new price): Use a breakthrough invention to establish a new market and price point that has never before existed (e.g., first-generation portable GPS unit).

2. Product improvement (enhanced product, same price): Expand functionality and demand—and maintain a profit—by providing ever-better versions of existing products without increasing manufacturing or distribution costs (e.g., latest-generation personal computer, smartphones).

3. Improved productivity (same product, reduced price): Through more efficient design or automation of production, reduce production and/or distribution costs and maintain profitability while reducing market pricing (e.g., flat screen television, robotic assembly).

The only way to capture and dominate any or all of these three areas is through innovation—either by means of the systematic application of human creativity to the design and engineering of new products, processes and techniques, or by way of the discovery of fundamentally new products and services through research.

Innovation is how productivity and growth happens. And that is why innovation is the dynamo at the heart of the modern global economy.

However, in today's economic landscape, where operational barriers—the previous mechanisms of ensuring a return on investment—are disappearing, innovation alone is no longer sufficient to ensure financial value creation. What is now required is invention.

Before we go any further, please note that we are using a more precise definition of invention than that found in everyday conversation. In normal language, innovation and invention are often treated as synonyms. For our purposes, however, we are being much more rigorous about these terms. In particular, we use innovation to describe the process of coming up with a new idea, converting that idea into a real world object or process, and then taking that object or process to the point of bringing an actual product or service to market. In the case of invention, we are applying a legal definition: when an innovation obtains full legal recognition as being a fundamentally new creation (i.e., it receives a patent or is treated as a trade secret) it moves from an unprotected position as an innovation to enjoying protection under the legal umbrella of being officially labeled an invention.

The concept of granted monopolies is not new. America's Founding Fathers chafed under an English-based patent system that was available only to aristocracy and granted at a very high cost. Not surprisingly, their vision for America included an inclusive and affordable patent system; their goal, effectively, was to ensure an invention democracy. As a result, patents are explicitly discussed in the Constitution itself, in Article I, Section 8:

The Congress shall have power . . . [t]o promote the progress of science and useful arts, by securing for limited times to authors and inventors the exclusive right to their respective writings and discoveries.

It is not surprising, then, that one of the first acts of the new Congress after the ratification of the Constitution was the passage in April 1790 of the Patent Act, which officially protected inventions. Just four months later, the first US patent was granted to Samuel Hopkins, who had invented a new method of producing potassium carbonate (potash). The patent was signed by President George Washington and Secretary of State Thomas Jefferson.

Thus begun a second American revolution, one of business expansion and wealth creation such as the world had never before seen. Statistical research and the resulting data not only confirms this observation but bears out the fact that the wealth-creating effects of innovation and invention are not linear but exponential in nature. Invention drove America's industrialization, which in turn fostered even more invention.

The story of patents is the story of American history. Thousands, then millions, of filings were made to the United States Patent and Trademark Office throughout the nineteenth and twentieth centuries, propelled by the industrialization of New England, the rise of the railroads, the Civil War, the opening of the West and the nation's arrival on the global stage. Each event, in turn, opened up a new horizon of opportunities for invention.

The end of the nineteenth century also produced the most famous declaration ever made regarding patents: "Everything that can be invented has been invented." Recent research suggests the remark—attributed to Charles Holland Duell, commissioner of the US patent office—is apocryphal, but it endures because it seems to fit both the era and the irony of what followed. It also captures another philosophical thread of the era: that human invention and innovation simply couldn't maintain such a fevered pace. (In fact, it is likely that the comment originated with Henry Ellsworth, who preceded Duell as commissioner of the patent office more than half a century earlier, and once stated that "The advancement of the arts, from year to year, taxes our credulity and seems to presage the arrival of that period when human improvement must end.")

It wasn't until 1870 that the first clue to the change afoot surfaced when Congress, as part of the larger reorganization of the patent office, voted to end the requirement that physical models be included in patent applications. The reason behind this alteration can be traced to the defining technical event of the era, the Centennial International Exposition of 1876, which was held in Philadelphia and featured perhaps the greatest gathering of new machinery and mechanical inventions ever, including the giant Corliss engines that powered the entire main hall. The real star of the show, however, was Alexander Graham Bell's new telephone, an invention that could only really be understood via blueprints and at least some training in physics.

This revolutionary shift in invention was underscored just a few months later with the announcement of Thomas Edison's incandescent electric light bulb. Suddenly, important inventions could no longer be explained with a simple model—and often not even through a schematic. This represented not just a fundamental transformation in terms of technology and invention, but also in the notion of intellectual capital. Innovation—the world of ideas—was increasingly being separated from invention—that is, from physical things.

By the early twentieth century, a sizable percentage of all new patents—including for the triode vacuum tube, wireless radio, television, radar and computers—were being awarded for new technologies that had not yet been fully implemented. The "thingness" of patents, once manifest in physical models that were increasingly becoming collectors' items, began to disappear. Over time, that "thingness" was replaced by a patent application process that was becoming an ever more intellectual exercise.

Who better equipped to write the new type of application than someone trained in careful and precise narration? Hence the rise of the patent attorney, a profession that today—when a single word can determine whether or not a patent filing will find the narrowest of open niches or survive a legal challenge of validity—acts as the gatekeeper to almost every one of the millions of patent applications filed worldwide each year.

Large companies quickly realized they could use their financial clout to mobilize attorneys to build vast patent portfolios that staked out every permutation and variation of their in-house-developed technologies and new products. This in turn led to the rise of corporate and academic research laboratories, which were chartered for the sole purpose of expanding their sponsors' IP holdings. This was not a new idea. Edison's Menlo Park laboratory, after all, got its start in the 1870s. But these new laboratories—located at IBM, Stanford University, MIT, General Electric, Dow Chemical, and most famously, AT&T Bell Laboratories— were an entirely different animal: wide-ranging, highly equipped and professionally managed. By the 1930s they were producing new innovations that were destined to change the world. Thanks to the labs' many successes—not to mention the dedication of their legal departments— they would go on to generate thousands of new patents.

It was also during this period that big companies began to use their legal muscle to try to defeat smaller competitors through patent litigation. The most famous of these early patent infringement suits involved RCA and Philo Farnsworth, the inventor of the first all-electronic television system. After an RCA engineer applied for a patent for a television based, in part, on technology he learned about during a visit to Farnsworth's laboratory, Farnsworth sued. David Sarnoff, president of RCA, who well understood the value of controlling patents, responded by having his lawyers launch a series of court cases, all in an effort to invalidate Farnsworth's work. After years of litigation, the courts ruled in Farnsworth's favor and RCA acquiesced and paid him royalties. Farnsworth's victory was a rare exception, however—one of the few times the little guy won—but it came at a high cost. His lengthy legal battle, coupled with the outbreak of World War II, greatly limited Farnsworth's ability to market his invention before his patent expired in 1947, leaving him broken and bitter. History has mostly ignored Farnsworth, and as a result, RCA walked away with much of the credit for his invention—and nearly all the profits.

No wonder corporate America quickly began to incorporate IP into its competitive and legal strategy.

As for the research laboratories that flourished in the wake of companies using financial leverage to increase their patent portfolios, their considerable power was first made apparent in the innovative new weapons systems they invented, systems that ultimately helped win World War II. But their biggest impact was felt by the general public in the decades after the war, when the marketplace was suddenly overwhelmed by an explosion of new products and inventions: the transistor and integrated circuit, the electronic computer, consumer television, commercial aircraft—all that and more, and at a pace far greater than that seen at the peak of the nineteenth century's golden age of invention.

But the immediate post-war era also saw another deep economic downturn, and with it the usual backlash against patents. This culminated, in 1952, with yet another restructuring of patent law, one whose impact is still being felt today. As noted on the website The Business of Patents:

In this amendment, an inventor had to describe not only his invention but also the basis for its infringement. Furthermore, an invention needed to be new and useful, as well as "non-obvious" to be granted a patent. This amendment, which required patents to be non-obvious, was implemented to keep individuals from taking ownership or taking away from the base pool of knowledge in a particular field.[8]

At first glance, this change would seem to reduce the likelihood of spurious or insufficiently distinct patent filings. But, in fact, just the opposite occurred: Now competitors knew exactly what they were up against and the precise boundaries of where to file. That, in turn, would lead to yet another tactical revolution in patent competition in the decades to come.

The subsequent economic boom of the 1950s and 1960s swung the pendulum in the other direction, back towards support for inventions and inventors. It was during this era, when the US dominated the world both economically and militarily, that the legal strategy of IP portfolio development and management was largely perfected. Companies big and small (but mostly big) not only began to assemble vast IP portfolios—sometimes in the thousands of patents—but also learned to file multiple patents on small variations of the same invention, and then to file them in different nations around the world. In Europe this process was accelerated with the opening of the European Patent Office in 1978.

The focus on invention ended in the 1970s as companies in the same markets, which had long battled one other over patents and their infringement, began to keep their innovations hidden as trade secrets rather than turn them into published patents. The 1980s, in fact, saw this fight taken to a higher—that is, global—level.

The key innovators in this new war were the Japanese conglomerates. They largely created what would become a new profession among multinational corporations: patent intelligence, which entailed using teams of trained researchers to study the intellectual property of international competitors, both to spot weaknesses in the patent coverage of their innovations and to predict where they might innovate next—all with an eye toward filing their own improvement patents first.

This was the first time that IP research became not only a systematic effort by the business world to learn through patent filings about the research being conducted by competitors, but also a way to proactively respond to that research and its resulting innovations—and then beat the originators in attaining a patent, and thus ownership of the invention.

The 1980s, generally considered "pro-patent" in terms of US legislation, also saw two other important patent-related events. The first, in 1982, was the abolishment of the patent office's own court, the Court of Customers and Patent Appeals. It was replaced by the new Court of Appeals of the Federal Circuit. This was seen both as an improvement in the patent approval process and as a gesture toward increasing protection for patent holders.

The second was the rise of the use of patent portfolios as competitive weapons. With massive consolidations taking place in a number of industries, notably electronics, automotive and pharmaceuticals, desperate companies began to revisit the mountains of patents they had been awarded in previous decades. They then unleashed their legal departments to sue every potential violator they could find.

Beginning in 1995, every branch of the US government seemed determined to rewrite and rationalize the nation's patent system. The result was a welter of new laws, regulations and court decisions that ultimately seemed to just make matters worse. (Bear with us as we conduct a quick tour of the last two decades of zig-zagging US patent policy.)

In 1995, the US government agreed, as part of its treaty obligations under the TRIPS Agreement, to sign the Uruguay Round Agreements Act. Under this agreement, the duration of a patent in the US was extended from seventeen to twenty years, bringing the time span into alignment with the rest of the world.

Then, in 1998, the United States Court of Appeals for the Federal Circuit ruled that for an invention to be eligible for a patent it must produce "a useful, concrete and tangible result" (State Street Bank and Trust Co. v. Signature Financial Group, Inc.). This decision was seen as a victory for practicality (as well as a return to nineteenth century patent law), but also a loss for basic research.

In 2008, however, the Federal Circuit court ruled that a patentable invention merely needed to "transform an article to a different state of thing" (In re Bilski)—thus seeming to overturn what was now being called the "State Street test" for patentability.

Then, a year later, the United States Supreme Court tried to address the resulting confusion (Bilski v. Kappos) by holding that the "machine-or-transformation test" of In re Bilski was not the sole test for determining the patent eligibility of a process, thus confusing things even more.

That was just the start. Which is why one of the most important insights to take away from this book is that in recent years, the very definition of what can be patented and who should be awarded the patent has changed in a fundamental way.

In 2011, Congress passed, and President Obama signed into law, the Leahy-Smith America Invents Act, which represented the biggest change in patent law in more than a half century. It settled a century-old debate over patent filing primacy between the "first-to-invent" model and the "first-to-file" model. The former had long been the law in the United States, even as the rest of the world shifted to the latter. The primary appeal of the first-to-invent rule was an issue of fairness: why reward somebody just for getting to the patent office first?

The obvious problem was that determining who was truly the first to invent is very difficult. We recall a senior research lab manager who left blank pages in his notebook and retained the writing instrument used on the page preceding the gap in the book so he could insert "inventive material" that could be subsequently dated well before he had truly conceived of the idea. Invention back-dating if you will. Of course this is completely illegal, not to mention immoral. It is, however, extremely difficult to prove, and can result in years of interference proceedings—effectively "priority contests"—argued in front of panels of patent judges.

The first-to-file model was designed to erase all of that and replace it with a system that awarded whichever filing showed the earliest time stamp at the patent office. It offered a simpler, but not necessarily fairer, solution, given that first-to-file tilts the table towards better capitalized companies that have the finances to file multiple applications quickly.

Then in 2014, the Supreme Court issued yet another ruling, this one related to Bilski. Known as Alice v. CLS Bank, it only managed to confuse things further. At issue in the Alice case, which involved a computer-based electronic escrow service designed to improve financial transactions, was whether some new methodologies—that is, "abstract ideas"—became physical (and thus patentable subject matter) if they were implemented on a computer.

The case seemed straightforward: simply converting a process to code and running it on a generic computer failed the Bilski standard. However, the case became much more complicated and impactful. The notion of keeping codified abstract ideas from being patented had a lot of powerful supporters, including Google, Hewlett-Packard, the Electronic Frontier Foundation and IBM. Even so, the judges on the Federal Circuit Court filed seven separate opinions, evidence that a degree of confusion remained even among the justices.

In the end, the Supreme Court invalidated the patent. But its opinion in the case, written by Justice Clarence Thomas, was almost universally seen as greatly adding to confusion and uncertainty around patenting. As a result, controversy around the case continues even today.

As evidenced by the last one hundred years of congressional enactments and court rulings, patent awards operate within a dynamic rule-based system. The pendulum swings back and forth—pro-inventor to anti-inventor and back again. This makes charting your IP strategic course akin to landing a jet fighter on an aircraft carrier in high seas. It also means the value and utility of your company's existing patent portfolio is very much like an investment portfolio, subject to ambient conditions and changing rules and regulations.

To illustrate: In April 2016 we spoke with a senior IP executive at a greatly admired Fortune 50 technology company. The IP executive told us that a couple of months earlier, the company's CEO had asked him and his team the following question: What is the impact of the Alice decision on our company's (very large) patent portfolio?

The IP executive answered that he suspected for a significant percentage of the patents in the company's portfolio, the validity, enforceability and defensibility had been diminished. However, he could not say specifically which patents were affected, nor could he recommend what action the company should take. When we spoke to the company executive again, two months after the CEO had originally posed his question, the IP executive and his team were still unable to provide a more accurate answer. Typically, when a Fortune 50 CEO asks a question, you find a way to answer it.

Being unable to answer wasn't entirely the team's fault. That's because only now, as this book is being written, are data analysis tools emerging that can quickly and cost effectively provide answers to these questions. Ironically, what is needed is more invention (tools) in order to perfect invention (patents).

The takeaway here is that patents have been and always will be important in creating and maintaining corporate value, but the rules are nuanced and dynamic. As a senior executive or board member, you have to navigate your company through the various shoals and hazards that have emerged in the world of intellectual property. In the face of a concerted global effort to undermine those defenses, your best plan lies in speed and accuracy. You need to evolve your new innovations into new inventions faster and better than ever before. And you need to understand and more deftly surround your competitors' IP faster and better than ever before.

This rapid-fire transformation from idea to innovation to invention is not something you can impose by fiat. Rather, it must be implanted into every office and laboratory within your company until the process of practical application—Inventioneering—becomes second nature to every employee, from engineers to marketers to sales professionals—and to you.

You must start now—not just because your competition is gaining on you, but because your friends (in the form of strategic partners, fellow supply chain members, distributors and retailers) are as well.

| Patents have value. |

Chapter 8

Patents as An Essential Corporate Resource

T hat statement may seem self-evident, but the reality is that many companies behave as if they don't comprehend this reality. Even savvy companies often fail to understand that this value is far more than just the licensing fees or sale prices patents might command.

In fact, patents can be powerful tools for measuring the health of your company—as well as the comparative strengths and values of competitors. They can also materially affect the price of a company's stock. A quality patent portfolio can pose a competitive threat or act as a competitive deterrent. Patent filings offer a glimpse into a company's impending strategy, including new product development. They are also a quantitative measure of innovativeness. And a patent portfolio is a leading indicator of a company's management performance, not to mention a yardstick for those who drive its core innovation.

In this chapter we will look at each of these metrics in turn to gain a deeper understanding of how IP is, in fact, one of a company's most important—and least understood—resources.

We begin by noting that a healthy patent portfolio can serve as a proxy for a well-managed company and a healthy corporate culture.

This takes several forms. Company directors, for example, can look at the history, trends, inventor participation and magnitude of a company's patent holdings to determine whether the CEO and the management team have a high "patent IQ." Executives with high IP intelligence understand the importance of deriving value and reducing risk from three sources:

- Existing company patents
- Growing the portfolio and covering their company's new inventions with a family of patents
- Encircling competitors' inventions with improvement patents in order to build a strong defense and maintain a path to operating freedom

A CEO who has not done this—that is, has failed to cultivate a strong pro-IP culture in the company—leaves the enterprise in a dangerously vulnerable position.

By the same token, smart financial institutions also look at a company's patent portfolio as a way of evaluating its true financial and market strength. That's because IP can represent a potential source of value, especially in negotiations during a merger or acquisition. In fact, there often is a direct correlation between a company's IP "prowess"—as just described—and the company's market value multiple.

What this means is that if a board is not looking at the firm's patent portfolio and scrutinizing the CEO's management of that portfolio, it may be unable to recognize the true worth of the company—and thus also unable to ensure that the CEO is maximizing that value. As IP becomes the competitive battleground in the twenty-first century, failure by boards to fulfill these duties may be seen as tantamount to a failure of their fiduciary responsibility. (We'll discuss this subject more in the next chapter.)

There is growing recognition of the value of indirect assets. A recent MIT report found that small companies are sixty-four times more likely (note: times, not percent) to succeed over the long-term if they pursue and obtain intellectual property. This idea runs counter to the belief held by some business theorists just a decade ago that the pace of commerce was moving so fast that there was no reason for companies to file for patents, given that any IP would already be obsolete by the time it was awarded. Such Luddite-based beliefs proved to be yet another false prophesying of the death of the patent system. Instead, the intervening years have shown that in an era when IP is becoming the primary competitive advantage, an empty patent portfolio leaves a company uniquely vulnerable to obliteration by patent infringement suits and injunction commands.

While the MIT study focused on startups and small companies, its findings apply equally to new ventures within large organizations. The correlation between success and a well-thought-out, planned, staffed and managed initiative —which patents demonstrate—is not unique to small companies. The mere fact of the product team's participation in the patent process forces structure and discipline across the group in answering such questions as:

- What problem are we trying to solve?
- How is this problem being solved today?
- What is new and better about our methods for solving this problem?

When you think about it, it's obvious that giving serious thought to these questions—and the many others required during the patent process—prior to investing in a new corporate endeavor dramatically increases the chances of success, even if the patent application is never filed. Patents are a long-established measurement and proof of the novelty, rigor and professionalism that has gone into the planning of an initiative, as well as of the people who are leading it. A startup is a structure built around a single initiative. A large corporation is a structure built around a plurality of initiatives. At its most basic level, one is a microcosm of the other. In each case, patents serve as a proxy for the quality of the innovation and of the commitment and intellect of those leading the project.

A former colleague, Ed Zander, whose last executive role was that of chairman of the board of Motorola Corporation, practiced a valuable management tactic. Before a project was ever green-lighted, Ed required that his team prepare a press release announcing the product or service. That forced the project team to think deeply about the value proposition that future customers would have to judge. It's a great practice, one we continue to use to this day. Working though the patent process prior to project approval takes Ed's approach to an even deeper level.

If we told you that we could provide your company with your competitors' strategic plans, you'd probably think we were involved in corporate espionage. But we're not. Corporate innovation that becomes the subject of patent pursuit is usually important stuff, so wouldn't you like to know which of your competitors' moves are rising to that level? When one of your competitors buys a company, that purchase entails strategic decision-making, all of which requires a lot of due diligence that you will not have access to. Wouldn't it be valuable to know what that company is really buying?

In fact, a vast amount of publicly available information is available to you and your company on just such matters. You just have to know where to look—and care enough to do so. Patent filings are most often made public within eighteen months of their first filing date. As we've previously discussed, there are ways to keep filings private but that require foregoing the ability to file in a foreign country, a potential advantage that most large companies are loath to surrender.

Unfortunately, sorting through a competitor's patent filings is usually discouraged by in-house counsel. There's a very good reason for this, as your lawyers will explain, since knowledge of a competitor's inventions could result in a legal finding of "willful infringement," which could triple the damages your company might suffer in a lawsuit. Even though the standard to prove willful infringement has been dramatically increased in recent years, many companies don't allow their employees any access to this patent data. Ironically, a major impetus behind the establishment of the patent system was to accelerate the sharing and adoption of inventions, usually in exchange for a reasonable licensing fee. But then a lot of reasonableness has gone out of the system over the years. That said, there are ways to obfuscate and abstract the specific knowledge that might result in a willful infringement claim yet still gain competitive knowledge. (More on this when we get to Part III.)

No discussion about the creation of strong patent portfolios is complete without taking a position on patent quality versus quantity.

This debate is the natural result of the contradictions at the heart of the of corporate intellectual property strategy. On the one hand, it is a smart strategy to file for the strongest and most inclusive patents possible on your company's current products and future inventions. It's also a smart strategy to file patents surrounding your competitors' inventions with patent filings. In the best of all worlds you'd file all types, but in the real world, given the limitations on money, time and legal support, most companies only file patent applications for 25 to 30 percent of their inventions.

Even though the majority of large corporate entities are leaving two-thirds of their company's inventions unprotected, it's still fair to say that the corporate patent game for the last two decades has been one of quantity. Numbers matter most. Management assigns quantitative patent goals. Employee performance and incentive plans are aligned to numbers of patents. Both in-house and outside patent counsel are encouraged to file patent applications and prosecute patents to achieve quantitative goals. Why is IBM at the top of every patent list published? Because for twenty years IBM has filed and been granted more patents than any other corporation on the planet—ever. Indeed, it's highly likely that your company and the professionals in your own IP organization have a quantitative attitude towards patents.

There are some good reasons for their attitude. One is optics. Patent competitive landscape maps are generated showing dense thickets of patents covering all of the invention real estate that one might imagine. Competitors that see you have a massive portfolio are inclined to think: They've got so many patents, there must be something scary or threatening in there, so we'd better stay away. That's not a bad conclusion to establish in the minds of your competitors.

That said, filing endless patents is not only a costly strategy but it can also be counterproductive. Why? Because you may be creating a culture in your patent ecosystem in which your counsel is incentivized to continue prosecuting or maintaining an asset that is diminishing in value. Few companies have that kind of money to burn. Additionally, new technologies have emerged that incorporate natural language processing (NLP), machine learning and big data analytics that allow for the qualitative assessment of the largest existing patent portfolios.

Even considering these developments, we believe that filing multiple patents across areas of invention or expertise to ward off predators (or filing them around a competitor's patent to isolate it) can be a brilliant tactic, as the Japanese impressively showed in the 1980s. But we also are convinced that a strategy of filing endless patents just to rack up numbers is ultimately wasteful, distracting and self-defeating.

So, how to think about this? Your first goal should be to build and maintain high-quality patents—that is, patents that can survive litigation or any type of post-grant review—and that philosophy should in turn determine how many patents you file and where you file them.

Quality, of course, can be a nebulous term. So let's be more specific about two aspects pertaining to quality. A high-quality patent should have:

Foundational quality: We have covered this a bit, but it's really important. Your company's invention must be patentable. You already know that you can't patent something that exists in nature (rejected as a result of failure to meet the requirements of Section 101 of the U.S. Patent Act). The problem is that the rules change, so what was once patentable may no longer be patentable. Business process patents that might cover many of the software patents you have in your portfolio have now been deemed to be non-patentable material due to the Supreme Court ruling in Alice Corp. v. CLS Bank International. This does not just apply to applications you are filing now, but also to any previously granted and once-valuable patents sitting in your portfolio.

As an experiment, we had big data analytics run on the last ten years of patent activity from Google and Yahoo to see how their patents would fare in just such an Alice test. This assessment covered over eight thousand patents and applications, and found that over 12 percent of those patents would have a high likelihood of being invalidated in litigation or other tests of validity.

This patent portfolio report summary was produced by the TurboPatent Machine, and reveals the high level information found in a portion of Yahoo's patent portfolio. A full Patent Portfolio Report reveals portfolio issues in detail.

This patent portfolio report summary was produced by the TurboPatent Machine, and reveals the high level information found in a portion of Google's patent portfolio. A full Patent Portfolio Report reveals portfolio issues in detail.

TURBOPATENT®

Portfolio Report

ORGANIZATION:
Google

ASSETS ANALYZED:
2,769

Date Range
6/16/2005 - 8/4/2016

2,769
Total
Assets

PATENTS:
1,851

APPLICATIONS:
918

PROJECTED USPTO FEES:

$35.8M
All Assets

$4.15M
Assets with Highest
Severity Issues

$2.58M for Patents

$1.57M for Applications

11.6%
of Portfolio Assets
have HIGH severity issues

321
Portfolio Assets
have HIGH severity issues

205
Patents

116
Applications

HIGH SEVERITY ISSUES BY CATEGORY

Patents   Applications

CATEGORY	# OF ASSETS	% OF PORTFOLIO	# OF ASSETS BY TYPE
Quality	180	6.5%	117 / 63
Alice	44	1.6%	28 / 16
Zero Citation	12	0.4%	12
Title/ Assignment	106	3.8%	65 / 41

A quality patent must be something new—it must be "novel"—and "non-obvious." That is, it must represent a fundamentally new idea, not merely an obvious variant on an existing invention. Moreover, just because you get a patent granted does not mean it passes either the novelty or the non-obvious test. A patent examiner spends an average of six hours examining your initial patent application. About half of that time is spent looking for prior art (evidence that your invention is already known) that pertains to these issues. But trust us when we say that hundreds of hours will be spent looking for prior art and other issues that will eliminate or diminish your patent if it becomes subject to litigation. The patent office has made it clear that it is not responsible for the ultimate validity of your granted patent. Unfortunately, however, most organizations are incentivized to simply get something past the patent examiner so they can include those patents in their portfolios. Right now, no one is responsible for patent quality—until, that is, you find yourself in court.

A quality patent should be devoid of formal defects, such as basic grammatical and spelling errors and formatting problems. But there are many more serious issues that can dramatically reduce or even eliminate a claim. Because patents are complex technical documents that need to accurately cross-reference data within and across each section, it becomes difficult for human beings to keep track of everything accurately. It is common for patents to contain errors and omissions in numbering or reference to invention parts, language needed to properly support a claim, or the inclusion of language that can damage a patent (jokingly referred to as "patent profanity"). Other professions, such as engineers and software developers, have CAD systems that give them a powerful assist in addressing similar problems. But the patent legal profession has been resistant to the adoption of technology. Because price and quantity have been the priority, no one in your company is insisting that counsel provide the foundational quality needed to achieve patent survivability. These technical problems result from errors in the original filing or those introduced during the prosecution phase. Many of the errors survive the internal review and the entire examination process and end up encoded into the final patent. These defects remain perpetual targets for competitors and any others who can legally test your claims. If your company is dedicated to superior-quality products, why not also show the same obsession when it comes to patent filings?

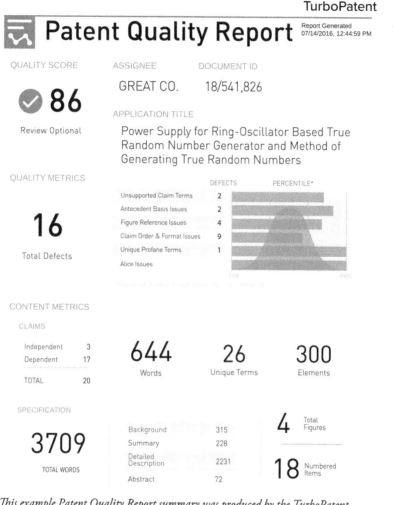

This example Patent Quality Report summary was produced by the TurboPatent Machine, and shows the high level information that might be found in an individual patent. A full Patent Quality Report reveals patent issues in detail.

1. Invention Quality and Market Applicability: This has less to do with process than with communicating a vision. It is one thing to file and earn a defensible and enforceable patent; it is quite another to file and earn a patent that is

actually congruent with the invention you are trying to defend. If the patent doesn't accomplish that task, all you've earned is IP protection for something you potentially never intend to build and something your competition probably does not intend to build. This miscommunication can happen at the outset of the process. While patent law is all based on the English language, the language of the inventor and the language of the patent professional are not always mutually understood. Which is why we often say that patent practitioners speak "patentese." To paraphrase George Bernard Shaw: Inventors and patent professionals are two peoples separated by a common language.

But this problem can also occur during the examination of the patent. Because getting any patent serves the quantity objective, those who are negotiating on behalf of the inventor often make significant compromises to obtain the patent grant. The result can often be something different and much less valuable than intended. Imagine setting out to lay claim to a city block in Manhattan and your lawyer comes back with a deed for a thousand square feet in Newark. Far better that you achieve harmony among patent, product and vision at the start.

The value of patents is not absolute because all patents are not equal. Sloppy, low-quality filings will reduce the value of your patents and potentially threaten your competitiveness over the long-term. Carefully prepared and edited—high-quality—patents offer the highest value and the best long-term protection. But even high-quality patents can be valueless if they don't accurately defend the boundaries of the inventions they were filed to cover. The good news is there are now powerful technological tools to enhance the quality of the patents your team creates, and for assessing the quality and viability of your portfolio on a continual basis.

So, how then do we actually—empirically—
determine the economic value of a patent?

The answer is, not easily—and for good reason.
Assuming your patent is technically sound, the value of
patents lies largely in the market value of the inventions
for which the patents are written or the potential cost to
the infringer if the ability to sell his product or service is
impinged. But inventions by definition are brand new,
and their full value lies somewhere in the future.

Take the microprocessor, arguably the greatest invention of
the twentieth century. When Intel filed for various patents on
the original processor models, the 4004 and 8008, how much
was that patent portfolio worth? At that time, not much.
But by the beginning of the twenty-first century, several
decades and many patents later, the portfolio was worth a lot.
By then, more than 20 billion microprocessors were in use
around the world and the devices were beginning to form the
heart of both the Internet and the smartphone revolution.
Thanks to Intel's near-dominance of the microprocessor
business protected by patents, its market capitalization by
2002 was the largest of any manufacturing company in
history, larger even than the entire US automobile industry.

Now, insofar as the history of IP goes, Intel may offer
an extreme example of patents protecting value, but it drives
home a point: Patent valuation is a mathematics problem,
it is not an arithmetic calculation. The calculus will always
be tricky, as the variables are many and the rate of change
is high. So, there are no simple mathematical formulas
we can give you. In any case, if you were to put a patent
portfolio up for sale you might get very different offers a
month from now versus today. The data below provides a
snapshot in time of the open market value of a patent asset.

The following data was reported by the ROL Group, LLC:

Asking Prices in the 2015 Market

Asking Price	Per asset (Pending or Granted)	Per US-issued Patents
Average	$189,880	$276,680
Min	$16,950	$30,000
Max	$925,000	$1 Million
Standard Deviation	$183,180	$249,290

*430 Data Points Analyzed for "Per Asset (pending or granted)" Data Set.
*423 Data Points Analyzed for "Per US-issued Patents" Data Set.
*Top and Bottom 5% of Data Points Removed from Each Set

(Source: Richardson Oliver Law Group)

This table shows market asking prices for patents and patent portfolios in 2015.

Finally, let's look at how the value of a company's patent portfolio helps to create its market value. We'll then consider scenarios in which patents can serve as financial currency.

Indeed, in many cases you can treat your patent portfolio as if it were actual cash.

Why? For one thing, if you sell (or spin out) your company, the market value of that new enterprise will be increased if it owns valuable patents. And even if you remain a stand-alone business, the presence of valuable patents in your IP portfolio directly correlates to an increase in your company's multiple and your share price.

There are strategies you can employ to best leverage your patents to better your company's financial situation. Here are two examples:

- You can write patents using a broad approach that might allow your company to generate licensing revenues via industries orthogonal to your own. For example: If you are in the aviation industry, your technologies might also be applicable to the auto industry. If that's the case, you should write your aviation-related patents broadly enough so that they can encompass the automotive industry. You then might have opportunities to license those patents to automotive businesses in addition to aviation firms, thus creating a larger revenue stream.

- You can use patents as collateral to borrow money at an advantaged rate. You can do so by working with a lender to establish a patent portfolio value. Providing this collateral de-risks the transaction, resulting in a lowered interest rate.

We hope that you're beginning to see that patents are much more than just rights granted to a company by the government. Patents can also provide information about your competition and their strategies and roadmaps.

The most important near-term benefit is that patents can increase your company's market value and create new revenue streams. And in the long term, such financial advantages will prove valuable during mergers, acquisitions and spin-offs.

At the same time, learning to value your patent portfolio is a double-edged sword, because while you may find that your company is more valuable and better defended than you thought, that same audit and valuation may also disclose that you are failing to innovate as well as you might, that your management of company IP is inadequate and that you are not obtaining a proper ROI on your patent portfolio. The very thing that could prove useful to you in improving your IP strategy and revenues could also be a red flag to shareholders that you are not fulfilling an important part of your job.

And that is yet another reason for this book. Better you find out your IP mistakes before your competitors and shareholders do—something we'll explore further in Chapter 9.

Throughout the book we have consistently noted that a company's board of directors not only has an important role to play in acquiring, managing and utilizing intellectual property, but that it also has a fiduciary responsibility in our increasingly patent-driven world to play those roles well—or risk dire consequences from both competitors and shareholders. When it comes to IP, boards today are more accountable than ever before.

Chapter 9

The Role of the Board

In this chapter we will look in-depth at the nature of this responsibility. In the first section, Board Accountability, we will look at the board's duty (which is also an opportunity) to sit in the cockpit of an enterprise and, after scrutinizing the dials and gauges that measure its internal operations, make key decisions that will make the business more innovative, better defended, and ultimately more competitive and healthy. We'll then follow up with Risk Mitigation, where we'll outline how to establish a strong defensive perimeter of patents, legal precedents and patent insurance. We'll also describe how to build a reputation that will help ward off trolls, scheming shareholders, foreign governments and other threatening parties.

Board Accountability

We begin by looking at patents as a means by which the board and senior management can quantitatively measure innovation. This is not a secondary concern: as market analysts and shareholders increasingly look at corporate innovation as a key metric in determining a company's value—and by extension the competence of its leadership—boards must be able to empirically justify their actions in this regard or risk punishment in the stock market.

There is another equally important impetus for today's boards of directors to continuously scrutinize their patent holdings: their fiduciary responsibility to manage risk. In one of the most important papers to date on the changing nature of board accountability, Ian D. McClure and Elvir Causevic recently wrote that "As patents are transacted, divested, litigated and strategically managed more frequently, the risk and value that corporate senior management and boards must monitor and take responsibility for is greater than ever before."[9]

These words should serve as a warning to all company boards, but most especially to companies that see themselves as industry innovators.

Most modern companies want to see themselves—and be seen by others—as innovative. After all, innovative companies are cool, and thus popular with customers and shareholders. At the same time, innovativeness also implies the potential to come up with something transformative that will blow the market apart, and in doing so, create an even bigger replacement market—thus rocketing a company ahead and leaving its competitors in the dust. That's why, even if a company isn't actually innovative, chances are—just look at any corporate annual report—it wants at least to be seen that way.

There are a lot of reasons why, despite the obvious advantages, most companies aren't really innovative. For now, we'll address one major reason for this failure: companies don't know how to measure innovation. After all, where do you look and what kind of yardstick should you use? How many PhD's are in your R&D department? How do customers see you as an innovator? Positive press clippings? All are useful, of course, but each is inadequate for the task, in part because these are all subjective measures.

As it turns out, the best quantitative measure of an organization's innovation is, in fact, its intellectual property. By looking at its patent portfolio—both as it currently stands and dynamically, over time—a company can come to appreciate its own wealth of creative and inventive talent, measure how quickly and effectively that creativity is put to work, and track how efficiently the company converts ideas into actual new products and services. This is a perfect task for the board.

It is also a task that can be accomplished rather quickly by applying certain key metrics to a company's IP, measuring (both in quantity and quality):

- Value of IP — In the last chapter we gave you some tools and techniques for measuring the value of your patents. So, the question now is: What is the total value of your IP? How does it compare with past years? You may currently hold more patents in your portfolio, but if they are of lesser value than your aging older ones, your company's innovation may be flagging. In addition, how does the value of your IP compare with estimates of your competitors' IP?
- Growth in IP — How many patents (and trade secrets) are currently in the company's portfolio? How many were added last year? How does that growth compare to the year before? Keep in mind that patents are a leading indicator of future development—today's patents are tomorrow's major products—so if your patent rate is declining, that's not a good sign.
- Growth of IP in relation to R&D spend — How many new patents does your company generate per $1 million dollars of R&D spent? This metric can not only tell you a lot about your company's ability to convert ideas to revenues, but it can also identify whether or not your R&D strategy is

misdirected or badly prioritized. Experience has shown that a good rule of thumb for this ratio is approximately one new patent for every $1 million to $2 million in R&D spent (see chart in Chapter 6). Obviously, there are variations depending on the industry, but if your ratio isn't close to this number, you have a duty to take a closer look.

You can't change a company's innovativeness by executive fiat. You can't just tell your R&D department to be smarter or cleverer or more inventive. Such transformations take time—and almost always involve firings and hirings, reorganization, and more carefully constructed and communicated strategies and goals. In some cases you may even discover that innovation has always existed but has been tamped down by bad management or a corporate culture that is risk-averse and hostile to new ideas. In other words, it could be your fault or the fault of your executive team.

Before you jump to any conclusions, however, you must first conduct an Innovation Audit like the one described above. But be prepared: As we will stress again and again in the pages ahead, creating a culture of innovation requires a considerable amount of managerial and executive courage. Why? Because it requires accepting greater risk. Some people, including certain individuals who are doing quite well in your current company culture, are not willing to accept that risk. As a result, they may not have a place in the new, innovative company you are preparing to build.

Competitive Predictors and Landscapes

Let's now look outside the internal operations of your company. How, as a board, can you use your IP assets—and your new understanding of patents—to help you compete against your industry counterparts and proactively defend yourself from their predations?

Here's an example of how the patent system can be put to use for competitive analysis and prediction: In most cases, patent applications become public eighteen months after they are submitted. What first appears as a bit of bureaucratic housecleaning turns out to be a powerful leading indicator of where your competition is going.

Track these public postings over time and you can essentially construct your competitor's patent and product strategy, and with enough lead time, effectively respond with your own patent filings. Your competitor's roadmap is available, free, via the United States Patent and Trademark Office. (But be aware that your own roadmap is available to your competitors in the same way.)

In order to better understand the competitive landscape and prepare your company for the road ahead, ask yourself six questions:

1. Who are your real competitors? Identify your competitors, and not just the obvious ones. Remember to keep an eye out for potential competitors who might move laterally across markets to attack you.
2. What are the product areas you're most concerned about? In addition to patents related to your current product line, scrutinize any new technologies that you are contemplating engaging long term.
3. Can you beat your competitors into the market? Now that you have a good idea of your competitors' roadmap, can you get ahead of them? Or do they have enough of a lead that they can enter that new market and set up IP defenses to hold you off?
4. Are there lucrative markets that your competitors missed? Look at their road map: Is there any white space where your competitors are not going? Are there opportunities there commensurate to

the one you will have to compete for? If so, why not own that other, less-busy space instead?

5. Can you use this knowledge to construct a defense? On the flip side, knowing that your competitors can see your IP if it is public should inform your own patent strategy such that you only disclose the information you want disclosed. One option is to keep your patent application under wraps by submitting it in the US only; file internationally and your application is required to made public. Keeping an application private all the way through to grant has the added advantage of ensuring continued privacy if a patent isn't granted. (If you opt for this strategy, remember to select the appropriate option on your application form.)

6. How do you prepare the battle space in advance? What do you need to do in terms of new patent filings, patent insurance, aggressive tactics, etc., to position any potential future litigation to your advantage? We'll look at these issues more deeply in the next section.

Board and Company Liability

We're now ready to discuss what liability a company's board of directors has in regard to the creation and management of company IP.

McClure and Causevic, whose warning about boards' growing responsibility for their company's patents was mentioned earlier in this chapter, see the evolving relationship of boards and company IP as emerging against the backdrop of what they call a historic shareholder awakening, in which corporate stockholders are becoming increasingly sophisticated about competitiveness, innovation and patents. "This shareholder awakening should in turn be eye-opening for corporate patent holders," they write in an article for Intellectual Asset Management. "With increased shareholder activism and sophistication about patent value and patent risks, corporations should ensure that they uphold higher accountability for patent risk-taking decisions, public information disclosures relating to IP information; and the importance of patent information to M&A and other material corporate events."[10]

Let's look more closely at each of these forms of higher accountability for boards:

- Patent risk-taking decisions: A quarter-century ago a company could assume that (a) a finding of actual patent infringement was difficult to prove given the difficulties for the claimed offender of doing a deep patent search (i.e., ignorance was still an excuse), and (b) patents held by anyone but direct competitors weren't a real threat. Today neither is true. Patents now are easy to search and are regularly used as articles of trade. Ignorance is no longer an excuse, and potential patent litigants can come from anywhere. Further, given that the average cost of litigating a patent suit runs between $2.5 million and $5 million, shareholders have little patience for boards that don't recognize vulnerable patents. It is estimated that only 4 percent of US companies can safely say that every patent risk-taking decision they make is not automatically also a material risk to the company. McClure and Causevic further note that "As the recognition of patent asset value increases, and as patent infringement filings rise in tandem with the fixed costs of patent litigation and the variable costs of losing, the duty to monitor excessive risk taking relative to patent infringement becomes even more important."[11]
- Public disclosure of IP information: In a world of ever greater government-mandated requirements for disclosure (e.g., Sarbanes-Oxley, Dodd-Frank) companies often find themselves in a quandary about

how much they are obliged to disclose about their IP holdings and how often they are required to update those disclosures. The dilemma lies in the fact that IP often adds considerable value to an enterprise, and that value must be disclosed to shareholders and potential investors. At the same time, as discussed earlier, too much disclosure can result in a company's strategic patent roadmap becoming visible to competitors. Just as bad, disclosure of a licensing agreement with a patent troll could open the door to other predators.

- The importance of patent information to mergers and acquisitions and other material corporate events: According to McClure and Causevic, "A director's core duties of care and loyalty—and the derived duties of good faith, confidentiality and disclosure—are important, if not highlighted, in the context of an M&A or other material corporate event."[12]

At the heart of every director's duty to his or her company is that of being fully informed "of all material information reasonably available" before making any decision that will have a material impact on the value and health of the company.[13]

A deep knowledge of the company's IP assets and their value at the time of a merger or acquisition would certainly seem to fit within that requirement. What that means in practice is that if a company is sold at a given price and subsequent events show that the company was wildly undervalued because the board didn't properly account for the true value of its IP, there will be more than reasonable grounds for shareholder litigation. Similarly, if that IP was wildly overvalued, the shareholders of the new owner would be well-positioned to make their own claims.

As a board member of either the buyer or seller in such a deal, it is incumbent upon you to do your due diligence and not only come up with a reasonable value for the IP of the acquired company, but also be able to make a strong case in support of that valuation.

Risk Mitigation

We finish this second section of the book with a closer look at how to reduce the risk of maneuvering the modern landscape of changing rules of patent infringement, patent litigation and patent trolls.

By this point, it should be clear that the world of patents, while offering enormous potential rewards, is also fraught with peril. At any moment, seemingly out of nowhere, you may be hit by a lawsuit accusing your company of patent infringement. Even worse, the very act of investigating in advance whether or not you might be infringing on anyone else's existing patents can rebound on you if the matter eventually goes to court. But worst of all is the litigation itself—which, as we have seen, can take years to adjudicate, cost millions of dollars and ultimately, at the eleventh hour, revolve around some minor or long-forgotten event.

No company wants to go through this nightmare, which is why managing and reducing risk has become one of the primary roles of twenty-first century boards of directors. The good news is that there is a growing body of tools, practices and support companies that have emerged in recent years to help with risk mitigation. These include techniques for taking the IP offensive to potential threats, purchasing one of the innovative new forms of patent insurance and spreading your patent portfolio to minimize the threat from a single legal assault.

Let's look at each in turn.

The Best Defense

The most important lesson of modern military theory is that mobility always overwhelms static defenses. And just as the age of castles and forts is now long gone, so too should be the notion that you can simply build a corpus of strong IP and it will hold off any infringement assaults from competitors, trolls, shareholders, standards organizations and others.

Smart companies realize that even when it comes to patents the best defense can be a good offense—or more precisely, a proactive defense.

Japanese tech companies in the 1980s were the first to systematize this technique. Recognizing that their superior-quality manufacturing prowess would enable them to hold industry leadership for a short time only—ultimately, they knew, the greater innovativeness of US tech companies would eventually see those companies leapfrog past them—the Japanese set out to find ways to anticipate, impede, and with luck, defeat American innovation.

The result was a concerted effort by Japanese industry to use patents in new ways as a form of competition. Their previously sleepy patent departments quickly took on a central role in the operations of these companies—first for intelligence and then against competitors.

Three of the techniques developed by the Japanese are not only still in use today, but have also taken on ever-greater importance.

- Encirclement: This technique is designed to stall a competitor's ability to innovate, even after it has been awarded a key patent. The process is simple: A company files patents relating to every variation and nuance of the competitor's patent, essentially encircling it and limiting its application. Figuratively speaking, the patent may exist, but it can't operate outside of a tightly circumscribed place. While undoubtedly powerful, this containment strategy is also expensive, requires considerable resourcefulness, and must be executed quickly before the competitor files additional, related patents and escapes the trap.

- Competitive Anticipation: A second technique tracks a competitor's technical papers, speeches, press coverage and, most important, patent filings in order to establish a trajectory for the company's future actions—all with a goal of beating it to the finish line. Think of anticipation as a kind of investigative, or forensic, patent work: Tracking the current actions of a competitor to extrapolate its next IP goal . . .and then filing there first. Competitively, this can be devastating. But it is also tedious work that demands a great deal of patience. Most of all, it requires having in-house talent as smart as that of the competitors you are tracking.

- Negotiation: A potential payoff of the first two techniques, negotiation can also be a strategy in and of itself. The goal here is to create trade bait—that is, to hold in your portfolio enough sufficiently valuable patents to be useful in negotiating a deal that reduces a competitor's potential threat. While some of those patents may actually be valuable to you, more likely you obtained them specifically for trade. Keep in mind that filing for a lot of patents that have little monetary value to your company requires deep pockets. Just as important, it is a strategy that necessitates a solid understanding of your competitor's current and future needs.

Patent Insurance

It may come as a surprise to know that there is, in fact, patent insurance. It is still a fairly new concept, can be very pricey (see below) and comes in several different forms. Nonetheless, patent insurance seems to be growing in popularity, suggesting that it might actually be worthwhile (although it is probably too early to draw any firm conclusions).

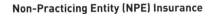

Non-Practicing Entity (NPE) Insurance

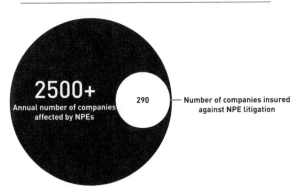

2500+
Annual number of companies affected by NPEs

290

Number of companies insured against NPE litigation

Although patent insurance is growing in popularity, few companies are currently insured against NPE litigation.

To date, patent insurance comes in two forms:

- Offensive Insurance: This is insurance for companies that want to "engage in litigation to protect and enforce their patent right."[14] These policies typically cover 75 percent of the enforcement costs of litigation up to a fixed amount (usually $500,000). Premiums for this level of coverage are about $4,000 annually. Policyholders are most often large companies.
- Defensive Insurance: This coverage kicks in when the holder is sued for patent infringement (think of it as "troll insurance"), so it is mostly purchased by startup companies and technology firms with extensive patent portfolios. The least expensive of these policies usually cover legal expenses only; more expensive policies cover

both damages and the cost of legal defense. Premiums are usually 2 to 5 percent of the coverage amount.[15]

An example of a patent insurer is the Silicon Valley-based RPX Corporation. RPX claims that since its founding in 2010 it has facilitated nearly a thousand patent suit dismissals and helped other clients avoid thousands of lawsuits. An interesting side activity of RPX's—and perhaps a glimpse into the future of the patent insurance industry—is that the company also purchases a lot of patents from its clients, only to turn around and license them back, thereby enabling clients to enjoy the benefits of those patents while leaving RPX to defend them. RPX calls this strategy "defensive patent acquisition."

Another example of a patent "insurance" is the LOT Network, a not-for-profit organization in which corporate members sign an agreement that provides immunity against patent assertion entity (troll) lawsuits if one of its patents should be transferred to a troll. LOT Network essentially takes over the legal ownership of the members' patents but still allows them to sell, license or transfer those patents as they see fit.

Is patent insurance destined to be the savior of corporate boards in dealing with their IP accountability? Yes and no. For one thing, you still must value your patent portfolio before you can determine how much coverage you need. Furthermore, you may find the fees too high for the protection offered. Law360, a legal blog, quotes attorney Christine Baker of prominent patent law firm Drinker Biddle & Reath as saying that "Clients need to consider the value of the IP as compared to their assets as a whole, how likely litigation may be, and how well they can absorb the cost of litigation. Because intellectual property litigation can be very expensive, clients may decide they would rather pay the cost of insurance, which is relatively predictable, than face the potential threat of a large, unexpected legal bill."[16]

Extending the Line

The third patent risk mitigation technique is the simplest (in theory) but often the most difficult in execution.

The theory is simple pragmatism: distribute your IP across multiple revenue streams. Why? Because if all of your IP is narrowly dedicated to single source of revenue, your company is hugely vulnerable to a single, well-placed attack. For example, if all of your revenue is derived from one patented technology, you are at high risk of a devastating takedown requiring only a single blow. You don't even have to lose the case. Remember RIM? The BlackBerry is proof that it only takes a protracted patent infringement case to paralyze even a giant company if all of its IP is clustered around a single business.

That's why you need to spread your defenses— or, in military terms, "extend your line." If your IP is distributed across multiple revenue streams, you are much less vulnerable to a single attack.

All of this should seem obvious. Too much of your company's revenue derived from a single product or concentrated among too few customers has long been considered risky business. So why, with the growing importance of IP today, should patent concentration be any different?

And yet many companies continue to fall into this trap. Why? Human nature. We want to protect what is most valuable to us. It's why we put money in the bank and jewels in a safe while leaving other valuable items exposed and at risk. With limited resources for IP protection, a company is bound to devote most, if not all, of those resources to protecting its crown-jewel inventions. This attitude is understandable, but it is also wrong. As we've seen throughout this book, no patent is entirely safe, and if your key patent goes down and you have failed to spread your IP protection, your company will be left legally naked and exposed—and potentially without the time and money to construct a new defense.

In the end, there are no easy answers. In the new competitive world of IP, you can no longer manage your patent portfolio by remote control. You need to get your hands dirty to understand what you do have and what you might create. Then you must determine how well you want to protect those assets. Finally, do the same exercise where your competitors are concerned, using the knowledge gained to better equip yourself to compete with them in the future.

We realize this isn't business as usual. Nonetheless, as a board member it is one of your most important duties, though not one that can be accomplished without effort. But as a smart and competent leader you are up to the task: that's why your shareholders have entrusted you with the job.

In Part III, we'll show you how to transform your entire company into a support system for your new IP strategy.

———

Part III – Introduction

In Part I we explained the several IP-related threats facing corporations today and how those threats are expanding. One of the threats is the decline of traditional operational barriers to market entry as they are replaced with technological advances that allow competitors to enter or redefine existing markets at a rapid pace. Additionally, trolls, activist shareholders, corporate competitors and even entire nations are now using intellectual property in ways that endanger businesses.

In Part II we provided a foundational education about patents and trade secrets: how they are earned, what they cost, the many forms that their value can take, and the fiduciary responsibility and accountability for directors related to IP.

In Part III our objective is to explain the proven best practices in each of the components that comprise the most effective IP strategy for you and your company. We will advocate for a departure from random methods of invention creation and bespoke approaches to patent preparation and prosecution. We are proponents of replacing these methods with modern technology-assisted engineering techniques. Your company will no longer draft patents—you will engineer them. But beyond the amalgamation of best practices, we also will instruct you on inculcating a powerful new invention culture that will penetrate the very DNA of your company: Inventioneering.

As with Deming's Total Quality initiatives, which changed the business world forever, Inventioneering requires broad corporate adoption, starting with the modeling of this culture at the very top of the corporation. Employees must believe patents and trade secrets are an essential and invaluable asset for a company. And they must see that belief embodied in the CEO, the board of directors and the senior leadership team.

Samuel J. Palmisano, former CEO of IBM, once said: "IBM isn't investing billions of dollars every year into research and development—and winning more patents than our top 10 competitors combined for more than a decade—as an academic exercise."[17]

Leaders don't just cultivate invention; the best ones are inventors themselves. Consider the following chart:

Great Leaders are Inventors

Organization	Leader/CEO	Inventions
Apple	Steve Jobs	100+
San Disk	Sanjay Mehrotra	70+
Amazon	Jeff Bezos	60+
Microsoft	Bill Gates	50+
Facebook	Mark Zuckerberg	50+
Google	Surgery Brin	30+
Microsoft	Satya Nadella	30+
Oracle	Larry Ellison	10+
Tesla Motors	Elon Musk	5
Stanford University	John Hennessey	5
United States of America	Abraham Lincoln	1

An inventive mind is a great leadership attribute.

If you think about it, this chart makes perfect sense. An invention is a creative, new and useful solution to a problem. It should not be surprising that the best leaders are inventors; they are leaders who understand how to create novel solutions to problems and also have the ability to recognize and motivate this talent in others. And as this chart shows, this doesn't just apply to leaders of corporations. Abraham Lincoln is not only considered the greatest of US presidents, but he is also the only one ever to be awarded a US patent.

Sanjay Mehrotra, CEO of SanDisk, who has been awarded more than seventy patents in his career, points to a vital connection between leadership and invention. Invention is "part of my DNA," Mehrotra told Forbes. It has "helped me a great deal in understanding the capabilities of our technology, and in assessing the complexities of the challenges ahead. That makes a big difference in determining strategic plans and in managing execution. It becomes easier to focus attention on the right issues."

Our approach in Part III is straightforward. We will convey in a step-by-step fashion the information that will allow you to transform yourself and your organization into a team of Inventioneers, which will enable your company to thrive in today's business landscape.

Before you set a course to your destination, you must know where you are now. Thus, we begin this section with an audit of your organization as it presently stands. What is the status of your IP? What are your IP practices currently in place? What is the attitude of the company toward IP? Who is involved and who is not? How invention-oriented is your company? How does your company stack up against the industry in terms of innovators and inventors?

Once you know where you stand, we will then provide a clear picture of your destination, focusing specifically on goals and objectives.

With the start and finish lines clearly understood, what remains is creating and setting the company IP strategy, generating an actionable plan and then executing that plan. As we have noted many times, patent portfolios are not a collection of static assets. Nor are IP strategies something to be set and forgotten. To remain viable, you must be vigilant in regularly measuring and managing your company's IP performance and applying agile readjustments as needed. The CEO and the leadership team must continuously model inventive behavior, reward that behavior in others and reinforce the Inventioneering culture that is being fostered.

Properly executed, this process becomes a virtuous cycle:

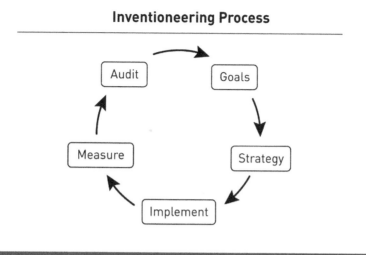

Inventioneering Process

Audit → Goals → Strategy → Implement → Measure → Audit

While technology has enabled new competitive approaches that can pose a threat to your business, it has also enabled the use of new and powerful tools and information to assist you in countering these threats by regularly assessing your IP circumstances and helping you attain a strong IP position. We will guide you in understanding the tools and how to use them.

Unfortunately (and ironically), there aren't yet a lot of tools. We say ironically because the professionals who comprise the patent legal industry—those, up to now, responsible for moving innovation to invention—have been woefully resistant to automation. Over the last thirty years the biggest technical leap forward in this profession has been the transformation from typewriters to word processors. Pathetic, but true.

Fortunately, recent technological advances in natural language processing (NLP), machine learning (a form of artificial intelligence, also known as AI), and data analytics are now being rapidly adopted by progressive corporations throughout the world. As a CEO, you no longer need to wait for the patent industry to catch up, or accept the excuses that leave your company blind when it comes to creating and managing a cost effective, high-quality IP strategy. Now you can create your own. We will discuss these technologies, tools and techniques in the coming chapters.

So, are you ready to become an Inventioneer? Are you ready to create the dynamic, innovative and competitive enterprise your company was meant to be? Are you ready to climb out of your defensive bunker and go on the patent offensive?

We know you are. The work requires commitment and patience, but these days there is nothing more invigorating in business life. We predict you will love it, and so will your team.

So, let's start Inventioneering.

> **"Study the past if you would define the future."**
>
> -Confucius

Chapter 10

The CEO Patent Report

When it comes to intellectual property, as the CEO you are being poorly served. Worse, it is probably your own fault.

Because intellectual property is thought to be both arcane and complicated, the task of understanding, planning and strategizing the company's IP is most often relegated to a group of specialists with legal backgrounds. These people are usually smart and well trained in their discipline, and thus essential to the company. However, their talents alone are no longer sufficient (if they ever were).

It's not unusual for employees to pursue short-term, narrow departmental metrics for, say, the legal department, and it may not be until ten years later, when the first lawsuits are filed against your company, that you learn that the foundational patents you built your company on are proven to be junk.

Trust us, there are a lot of useless junk patents in your patent portfolio. How do we know this? Because we have analyzed hundreds of portfolios and have found there are no exceptions. Why is this so? Because the incentives applied to those responsible for creating these assets have long been aligned with seeking credit now for filings that may blow up later—with luck, after they've retired. It's simply easier for those managing your portfolio to ignore the junk and have the company pay millions of dollars in maintenance fees (on average, each thousand patents in your US patent portfolio costs $1 million annually in USPTO fees), just as it's easier to stand by passively during the prosecution process as the patent application devolves into a worthless piece of paper.

As we said at the beginning, the problem likely begins with you. If you are not providing continuous oversight of your IP operations and you regularly applaud the number of patents filed and earned, you have undoubtedly created an environment that rewards quantity over validity, defensibility and value. You are getting what you (albeit unconsciously) asked for.

And these misdirected rewards only grow over time to include all stakeholders. The IP world is small and incestuous. Almost all internal IP organizations choose outside patent firms and practitioners who aid them in achieving these quantitative and efficiency goals, leaving validity, defensibility and value as unaudited assumptions.

When we ask corporate IP managers about the methods they use to ensure patent quality, the typical answer we get is, "We employ great practitioners and if they don't perform, we fire them." We then ask two follow-up questions: How do you actually measure the performance of your practitioners and the firms that employ them? And when was the last time you actually fired one of these firms?

The typical and content-free answer to the first question is, "They want our business so they always do a great job." As for the second, we are usually rewarded with the circular logic of "Almost never." The ugly truth is that outside counsel is often made up of ex-employees or past colleagues of patent managers within the company. Which means that everybody has a stake in maintaining the lucrative status quo while you remain in the dark.

Without objective measurement and oversight, the likelihood of real patent validity, quality and value is low. Can you imagine if your financial audits and quarterly and annual reports were handled in a similarly opaque manner? Someone would soon be doing jail time.

If you don't believe us, just ask your most senior person responsible for IP the following question: What percentage of the company's patent portfolio has de minimis value? If you get a number less than 20 percent, either you are being lied to or that employee is incompetent. An answer greater than 50 percent would be closer to the truth. On the other hand, if you hear something along the lines of, "It's a numbers game" or "Quantitative optics are important" or "Much of our portfolio is sending a market signal," understand this: you are being spun.

Mismanaged is the only valid description of a portfolio riddled with valueless assets that carry a significant cost burden. You would never accept this in your personal financial investment portfolio (you would fire your broker); neither would you accept it when it comes to your company's financial management and reporting (you would fire your CFO). Why then would you accept mismanagement of your company's intellectual property? Particularly now that you understand that IP is your company's most important asset.

For the rest of this chapter we have constructed an annotated sample audit. This audit document is populated with the data from a synthesized collection of information we have gleaned from more than one hundred companies (without, of course, divulging any proprietary information about the clients and companies interviewed). Our approach will give you a realistic example of the kind of report you should expect from your team. As the CEO, you should insist on just such an IP audit, require that it be updated quarterly and demand that it always be at your fingertips.

What follows may seem like a long list of questions to answer. But in our experience, you can digest this information in fifteen to twenty minutes every three months once you have done the initial review and established your reporting system. The initial review will take an hour or two, but it will be an excellent investment of your time. Keeping yourself regularly updated thereafter will give you a firm handle on one of your company's most important assets.

We highly recommend that you have your executive team and board of directors conduct this initial review and quarterly update as well. A further suggestion is to involve a third-party auditor for the initial information-gathering task, and then perform an annual audit using an outside organization. Just as with financial audits, it's simply good practice to have a neutral party with a fresh set of eyes and ideas compile the information.

The CEO Patent Report

The CEO Patent Report is divided into four sections:

1. A quantitative section that contains the hard data on your company's patent portfolio. This section also includes the IP budgetary information and the cost and value of your patent assets.
2. A strategy section that gives guidance in assessing the company's IP strategy, or lack thereof.
3. A process section that reviews the systems and methods the company uses to build and manage its IP portfolio and related matters.

4. A company patent culture and attitude assessment that spans the board of directors to first-level innovative contributors.

We suggest that you first read through the following report, studying the nature and range of the questions, and see how other companies answered them. The results that follow each question are not actual numbers for any one company, but are a composite derived from scores of companies. We also provide current industry averages and ranges that you might find useful in comparing your company's performance. Look at how the questions play off one another and consider what underlying truths about a company's IP they can expose and, ultimately, how they might change your perspective on the role of IP management.

The next step is to pull together your senior team and conduct this audit on your own company. Set aside a couple of hours to get it right; we guarantee that just that effort alone will have a profound effect upon your organization and how you do business in the future.

Good luck, and we'll see you after you review the report.

CEO Patent Report

Great Corp.

Quantitative Audit	2
Strategy Audit	11
Process Audit	12
Cultural Audit	20

Prepared on 5/24/2016 by TurboPatent Corp using TurboPatent Analytics

Quantitative Audit

01 How many active US patents are in the company portfolio?
a. Percent created by your company?
b. Percent acquired directly or via M&A?

Active U.S. patents:

4886

Active US patents

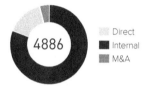

- Direct
- Internal
- M&A

Internal: 3225 patents - 66%
Direct Acquisition: 1234 patents - 23%
Mergers and Acquisitions: 537 patents - 11%

Active U.S. patents by technology center

- Manufacturing
- Software
- Hardware

Software: 2687 patents - 56%
Hardware: 1612 patents - 32%
Manufacturing: 586 patents - 12%

02 How many pending US patent applications are in process at this time?
a. Percent created by your company?
b. Percent acquired directly or via M&A?
c. How many patent applications have been filed in each of the last three years?

Pending U.S. applications:

1289

Pending U.S. applications

- ■ M&A
- ▨ Direct
- ■ Internal

Internal: 1070 - 83%
Direct Acquisition: 129 - 10%
Mergers and Acquisitions: 90 - 7%

Pending U.S. patents by technology center

- ■ Manufacturing
- ▨ Hardware
- ■ Software

Software: 722 patents - 56%
Hardware: 412 patents - 32%
Manufacturing: 155 patents - 12%

Number of patent applications filed in the last three years

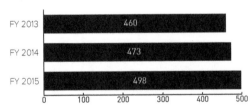

03 How many granted international patents are in the company portfolio?
a. Percent breakdown by country?

04 How many pending applications are in process outside of the U.S.?
a. Percent breakdown by country?

Pending international:	Granted international:
390	**1584**

Granted patents and pending applications by country

Asia

	Granted	Percentage		Pending	Percentage
China	357	22.5%	China	98	25.1%
South Korea	241	15.2%	South Korea	29	7.4%
Taiwan	182	11.5%	Taiwan	59	15.1%
Japan	104	6.6%	Japan	24	6.2%

South Pacific

	Granted	Percentage		Pending	Percentage
Singapore	241	15.2%	Singapore	76	19.5%
Malaysia	159	10.0%	Malaysia	63	16.2%
Australia	55	3.5%	Australia	8	2.1%
New Zealand	55	3.5%	New Zealand	3	0.8%

Europe

	Granted	Percentage		Pending	Percentage
European Union	124	7.8%	European Union	20	5.1%
Great Britain	44	2.8%	Russia	5	1.3%
Germany	24	1.5%	Great Britain	2	0.5%
Russia	18	1.1%	Netherlands	3	0.8%

Report prepared by TurboPatent Corporation using TurboPatent® Analytics

05

What is the estimated overall development cost (investment) and acquisition cost of the company's US patent portfolio including all in progress applications?

- ■ Software $193.1M
- Hardware $115.8M
- ■ Manufacturing $42.1M

Total development and acquisition cost is $351 million. $292.8M for internal development with $230.1M for granted applications and $62.7M for pending application. $58.2 M for acquisitions with $44.8 for granted applications and $13.4M for pending applications.

Development — $230.1M — $62.7M — **$292.8M**

Acquisition — $44.8M — **$58.2M** — $13.4M

- ■ Granted
- In Progress

Software

Development — $126.6M — $34.5M — **$161.0M**

Acquisition — $24.6M — **$32.0M** — $7.4M

Hardware

Development — $60.7M — $16.5M — **$77.2M**

Acquisition — $29.7M — **$38.6M** — $8.9M

Manufacturing

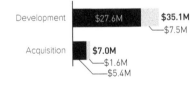

Development — $27.6M — **$35.1M** — $7.5M

Acquisition — **$7.0M** — $1.6M — $5.4M

06 Estimated overall development cost of the international patent portfolio (including all in progress applications)
a. Percent breakdown by country

Estimated overall development cost

Overall development cost of the international patent portfolio is estimated at $119,640,000 with $96.2 million attributed to granted applications and $23.4 million attributed to pending application. Asia leads in regional development costs at $65.6 million with China attributed with 22.8% of total international costs.

$23.4M

$119 Million

■ Granted 80.4%
▨ Pending 19.6%

$96.2M

$119 Million

■ Asia $65.6M
▨ South Pacific $39.6M
■ Europe $14.4M

Estimated development cost percent breakdown by country

Asia

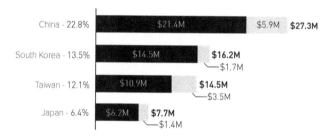

China - 22.8% $21.4M $5.9M **$27.3M**

South Korea - 13.5% $14.5M   **$16.2M**
            $1.7M

Taiwan - 12.1% $10.9M   **$14.5M**
            $3.5M

Japan - 6.4% $6.2M   **$7.7M**
            $1.4M

South Pacific

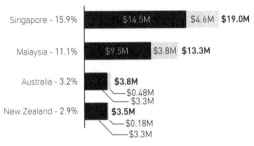

Singapore - 15.9% — $14.5M | $4.6M | **$19.0M**

Malaysia - 11.1% — $9.5M | $3.8M | **$13.3M**

Australia - 3.2% — **$3.8M**
$0.48M
$3.3M

New Zealand - 2.9% — **$3.5M**
$0.18M
$3.3M

Europe

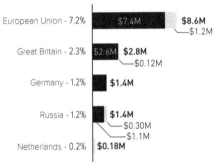

European Union - 7.2% — $7.4M | **$8.6M**
$1.2M

Great Britain - 2.3% — $2.6M | **$2.8M**
$0.12M

Germany - 1.2% — **$1.4M**

Russia - 1.2% — **$1.4M**
$0.30M
$1.1M

Netherlands - 0.2% — **$0.18M**

144

07   What is the estimated market value of the company's aggregate patent
portfolio?

Total Portfolio Value

$439,275,000

Average Patent Value

$55,097

Portfolio Value
(in millions)

United States	$293M	$322.136M
		$29M
Other Countries	$103M	$117.14M
		$14.1M

■ Granted
▨ Pending

Portfolio Breakdown

	Pending Portfolio Value	Granted Portfolio Value	Total Portfolio Value	Total Pending and Active Applications
United States	$29,130,000	$293,006,000	$322,136,000	5857
Other Countries	$14,100,000	$103,040,000	$117,140,000	1952 (original) /1891 (foreign equivalents)

Report prepared by TurboPatent Corporation using TurboPatent® Analytics

What is the company's aggregate annual budget for the development of patent and trade-secret assets for the last three years?
a. Breakdown between government fees, legal fees (inside and outside counsel, and other costs)

Aggregate Annual Budget

2013	2014	2015
$42,000,000	**$45,500,000**	**$60,000,000**

Budget Breakdown
(in thousands)

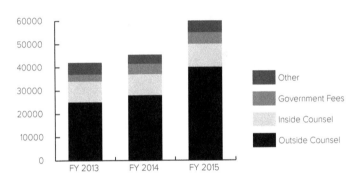

Budget Breakdown
(in thousands)

	FY 2013	FY 2014	FY 2015
Legal Fees			
12	$9,000 - 21%	$9,000 - 20%	$10,000 - 17%
Outside Counsel	$25,000 - 60%	$28,000 - 61%	$40,000 - 67%
Government Fees	$3,000 - 7%	$4,500 - 10%	$3,000 - 8%
Other	$5,000 - 12%	$4,000 - 9%	$5,000 - 8%
Total	$42,000	$45,000	$60,000

09 How many U.S. patents has the company been awarded in each of the last three years?

Patents Awarded in Last Three Years

2013	2014	2015
293	301	313

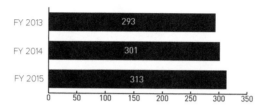

10 How many patent assets have been abandoned in each of the last three years?
   a. Pending applications abandoned in each of the last three years?
   b. Granted patents abandoned in each of the last three years?

Patent Assets Abandoned in Last Three Years

2013	2014	2015
218	227	238

10   Report prepared by TurboPatent Corporation using TurboPatent® Analytics

11 What percentage of submitted inventions are not pursued as patent applications?

The percentage of submitted inventions that are not pursued as patent applications is 62%

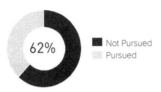

Not Pursued
Pursued

12 What is the average amount of time to get a patent on file from the point of first identifying the invention?

Average amount of time from identification to filing is 221 days

Qualitative Audit

01   a. What is a breakdown of strengths and issues for the patent portfolio?
b. What are the projected USPTO fees?

Patent Portfolio Issue Report

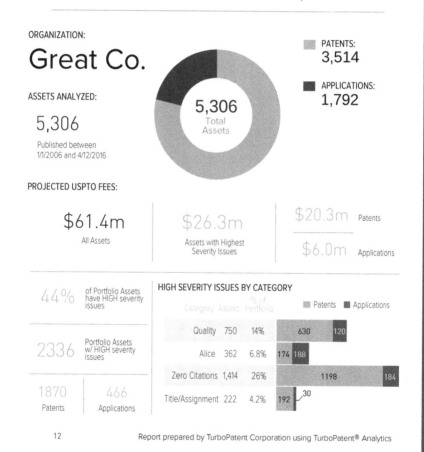

ORGANIZATION:

Great Co.

ASSETS ANALYZED:

5,306

Published between
1/1/2006 and 4/12/2016

PATENTS:
3,514

APPLICATIONS:
1,792

5,306
Total
Assets

PROJECTED USPTO FEES:

$61.4m	$26.3m	$20.3m Patents
All Assets	Assets with Highest Severity Issues	$6.0m Applications

44% of Portfolio Assets have HIGH severity issues

2336 Portfolio Assets w/ HIGH severity issues

1870 Patents   466 Applications

HIGH SEVERITY ISSUES BY CATEGORY

■ Patents   ■ Applications

Category	Assets	% of Portfolio	Patents	Applications
Quality	750	14%	630	120
Alice	362	6.8%	174	188
Zero Citations	1,414	26%	1198	184
Title/Assignment	222	4.2%	192	30

12   Report prepared by TurboPatent Corporation using TurboPatent® Analytics

Issue Summary

All Assets

Category	Assets	% of Portfolio	USPTO Fees
Quality	4,762	90%	$54.7m
Alice	2,026	38%	$23.1m
Zero Citations	2,420	46%	$30.4m
Title/Assignment	902	17%	$9.3m
Unique Assets	**5,170**	**97%**	**$59.7m**

Patents

Category	Patents	% of Patents	USPTO Fees
Quality	3,292	94%	$35.5m
Alice	1,290	37%	$13.5m
Zero Citations	1,450	41%	$17.6m
Title/Assignment	614	17%	$5.8m
Unique Assets	**3,464**	**99%**	**$37.5m**

Applications

Category	Applications	% of Applications	USPTO Fees
Quality	1,470	82%	$19.1m
Alice	736	41%	$9.5m
Zero Citations	970	54%	$12.8m
Title/Assignment	288	16%	$3.5m
Unique Assets	**1,706**	**95%**	**$22.2m**

Quality Issues Summary

All Assets

Severity	Assets	% of Portfolio	USPTO Fees
Low	1,900	36%	$22.6m
Moderate	2,112	40%	$24.3m
High	750	14%	$7.8m
Total Assets	**4,762**	**90%**	**$54.7m**

Patents

Severity	Patents	% of Patents	USPTO Fees
Low	1,218	35%	$13.7m
Moderate	1,444	41%	$15.6m
High	630	18%	$6.3m
Total Patents	**3,292**	**94%**	**$35.5m**

Applications

Severity	Applications	% of Applications	USPTO Fees
Low	682	38%	$8.9m
Moderate	668	37%	$8.7m
High	120	7%	$1.5m
Total Applications	**1,470**	**82%**	**$19.1m**

14   Report prepared by TurboPatent Corporation using TurboPatent® Analytics

Assets By Category Count

All Assets

Category Count	Assets	% of Portfolio	USPTO Fees
0 Categories	136	3%	$1.7m
1 Categories	1,672	32%	$18.8m
2 Categories	2,202	42%	$25.8m
3 Categories	1,150	22%	$13.4m
4 Categories	146	3%	$1.7m

Patents

Category Count	Patents	% of Patents	USPTO Fees
0 Categories	50	1%	$52.4k
1 Categories	1,168	33%	$12.3m
2 Categories	1,490	42%	$16.5m
3 Categories	726	21%	$7.8m
4 Categories	80	2%	$92.4k

Applications

Category Count	Applications	% of Applications	USPTO Fees
0 Categories	86	5%	$1.1m
1 Categories	504	28%	$6.5m
2 Categories	424	24%	$9.3m
3 Categories	424	24%	$5.6m
4 Categories	66	4%	$78.1k

Alice Issues - Patents

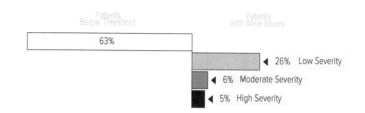

Patents Below Threshold **63%**

Patents with Alice Issues

◀ 26% Low Severity
◀ 6% Moderate Severity
◀ 5% High Severity

Alice Issues vs. Projected Fees

	Patents	% of Patents	USPTO Fees
Low Severity	922	26%	$9.8m
Moderate Severity	194	6%	$2.0m
High Severity	174	5%	$1.7m
Patents with Alice Issues	1,290	37%	$13.5m

Alice Issues vs. Citation Count

	Below Alice Issues Threshold	Low/Moderate Severity Alice Issues	High Severity Alice Issues
≥10 Citations	168	142	28
Zero Citations (> 3 years)	774	364	60

Report prepared by TurboPatent Corporation using TurboPatent® Analytics

Alice Issues - Applications

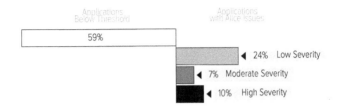

Applications Below Threshold	Applications with Alice Issues
59%	
	◄ 24% Low Severity
	◄ 7% Moderate Severity
	◄ 10% High Severity

Alice Issues vs. Projected Fees

	Applications	% of Applications	USPTO Fees
Low Severity	426	24%	$5.4m
Moderate Severity	122	7%	$1.6m
High Severity	188	10%	$2.5m
Applications with Alice Issues	736	41%	$9.5m

Alice Issues vs. Citation Count

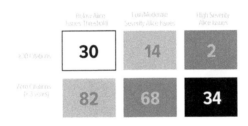

	Below Alice Issues Threshold	Low/Moderate Severity Alice Issues	High Severity Alice Issues
>30 Citations	30	14	2
Zero Citations (0-3 years)	82	68	34

Citation Summary

Patents

338	1,726	232	1218
10% ≥30 Citations	**48%** 1-29 Citations	**7%** Zero Citations (> 3 Years)	**34%** Zero Citations (> 3 Years)

	Patents	Citations	% Citation	USPTO Fees
Entire Portfolio	3,514	43,314	100%	$38.1m
30+ Citations	338	32,732	76%	$1.8m
1-29 Citations	1,726	10,582	24%	$18.6m
Zero Citations <3 years	232	0	0%	$2.9m
Zero Citations >3 years	1218	0	0%	$14.7m

Applications

46	776	774	196
3% ≥30 Citations	**43%** 1-29 Citations	**44%** Zero Citations (< 3 Years)	**10%** Zero Citations (> 3 Years)

	Applications	Citations	% Citation	USPTO Fees
Entire Portfolio	1,792	7,122	100%	$23.4m
30+ Citations	46	2,660	37%	$56.8m
1-29 Citations	776	4,462	63%	$10.0m
Zero Citations <3 years	774	0	0%	$10.3m
Zero Citations >3 years	196	0	0%	$2.5m

Report prepared by TurboPatent Corporation using TurboPatent® Analytics

Topic Summary

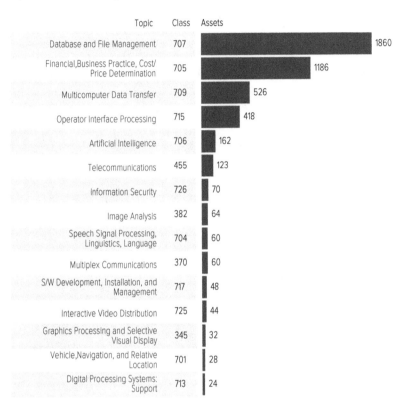

Topic	Class	Assets
Database and File Management	707	1860
Financial,Business Practice, Cost/Price Determination	705	1186
Multicomputer Data Transfer	709	526
Operator Interface Processing	715	418
Artificial Intelligence	706	162
Telecommunications	455	123
Information Security	726	70
Image Analysis	382	64
Speech Signal Processing, Linguistics, Language	704	60
Multiplex Communications	370	60
S/W Development, Installation, and Management	717	48
Interactive Video Distribution	725	44
Graphics Processing and Selective Visual Display	345	32
Vehicle,Navigation, and Relative Location	701	28
Digital Processing Systems: Support	713	24

Title/Assignment Issues

All Assets

Severity	Assets	% of Portfolio	USPTO Fees
None	4,404	83%	$52.1m
Low/Moderate	680	13%	$7.9m
High	222	4%	$1.3m
Total Assets	**5,306**	**100%**	**$61.4m**

Patents

Severity	Patents	% of Patents	USPTO Fees
None	2,900	83%	$32.3m
Low/Moderate	422	12%	$4.8m
High	192	6%	$96.4m
Total Patents	**3,514**	**100%**	**$38.1m**

Applications

Severity	Applications	% of Applications	USPTO Fees
None	1,504	84%	$19.9m
Low/Moderate	258	14%	$3.1m
High	30	2%	$35.9m
Total Applications	**1,792**	**100%**	**$23.4m**

Report prepared by TurboPatent Corporation using TurboPatent® Analytics

Citations by Corporation

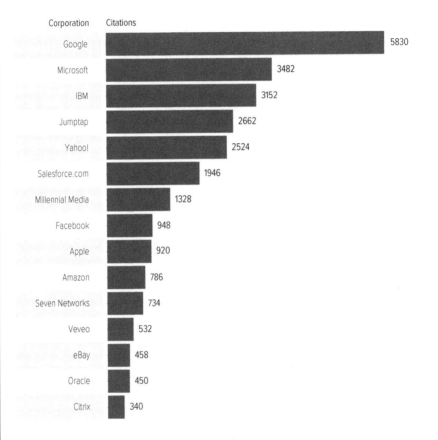

Corporation	Citations
Google	5830
Microsoft	3482
IBM	3152
Jumptap	2662
Yahoo!	2524
Salesforce.com	1946
Millennial Media	1328
Facebook	948
Apple	920
Amazon	786
Seven Networks	734
Veveo	532
eBay	458
Oracle	450
Citrix	340

02

Who are the top ten outside counsel (by volume) and how well do they perform?

Top ten outside counsel by volume account for 34% (439) of the total 1289 US pending applications.

Average efficiency score of top 10:	88.4
Average efficiency score of all outside counsell:	56.6
Average quality score of top 10:	77.5
Average quality score of all attorneys:	66.3

attorney	firm	total applications	attorney allowance rate	allowance rate vs mean	quality score	efficiency metric	review indicator
Malcolm Reynolds	Reynolds, Washburn and Cobb	241	80%	+45%	93	92	✓
Lani Tupu	Warwick Davis	255	56%	+18%	89	88	✓
Ben Sisko	Picard, Sisko and Pike	253	71%	+30%	92	83	✓
Kathryn Mullen	Warwick Davis	220	65%	+27%	90	91	✓
David Greenaway	Warwick Davis	219	61%	+23%	75	89	⚠
Jayne Cobb	Reynolds, Washburn and Cobb	218	55%	+20%	90	91	✓
Don Austen	Warwick Davis	210	61%	+22%	90	86	⚠
Jake Sisko	Picard, Sisko and Pike	205	10%	-30%	42	92	✗
Kristine Kochanski	Kryten Kochanski	204	65%	+30%	74	95	⚠
Arnold Rimmer	Kryten Kochanski	201	48%	-4%	40	77	✗

Report prepared by TurboPatent Corporation using TurboPatent® Analytics

Strategy Audit

Which one of these strategies or combination of strategies does your company employ? Which is the primary strategy?

The primary strategy is an Aligned Patent Strategy (60%), followed by Defensive (30%) and Revenue Strategies (10%)

1. Reactive Patent Strategy

The company does not have a formalized patent strategy that has been reviewed and understood by the executive team and the BOD, then the company is operating tactically with respect to patents.

30%

2. Defensive Patent Strategy

The primary goal of the company is to use its patent portfolio as a method for maintaining a "freedom to operate", meaning to market and sell its products with minimal disruption from its competitors

3. Offensive Patent Strategy

The company uses its patent portfolio to stop fast-following copy cats from entering the market and stealing share or applying price pressure to their product and services.

10%

4. Revenue Patent Strategy

The company uses its patent portfolio, through the licensing or sales of its IP, as a method of generating revenues that contribute directly to the bottom line. Companies like Microsoft and Oracle have generated in excess of $5B from IP licensing in given years.

60%

5. Aligned Patent Strategy

Creating a patent and trade-secret strategy that follows and supports the corporate strategy. Typically a company has a strategic plan that when executed will increase revenues and profits, increase market share and/or open new markets, and ensure a sustainable competitive advantage. An Aligned Patent Strategy would directly support these plans and objectives.

6. Inventioneering

Process Audit

01
Who on your staff is responsible for the patent and trade-secret organization, budget, and process?

Lead staff member responisble for patent and trade-secret organization, budget and process is Esteban Sorrento-Gillis

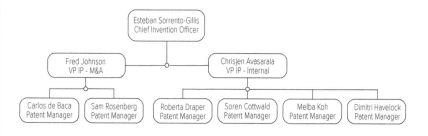

02
What is the process for establishing the patent budget?
a. Establish budget as a ratio of R&D spend?
b. Establish quantity patent target and compute budget?
c. Match competitors patent rates and dollar spend?

Patent budget is $60,328,000
This is allocated as 0.8% of the R&D budget.

R&D Budget

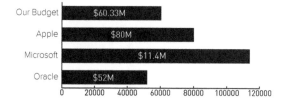

24   Report prepared by TurboPatent Corporation using TurboPatent® Analytics

03

What is the process and system for obtaining inventions from employees?
a. Invention Disclosure system?
b. Brainstorming/Ideation sessions?
c. Invention assistance from company's IP organization?
d. Open Invention processes?

Invention Disclosure - 40%
Brainstorming/Ideation sessions - 23%
Assistance From IP Counsel - 15%
Open Invention - 6%

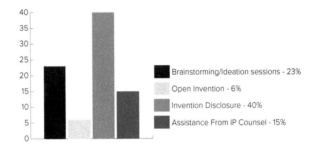

Brainstorming/Ideation sessions - 23%
Open Invention - 6%
Invention Disclosure - 40%
Assistance From IP Counsel - 15%

04 When in the product development life cycle is the invention disclosure usually initiated and completed?
   a. Concept phase?
   b. Design phase?
   c. Build phase?
   d. Launch planning phase?
   e. Post launch?

Invention disclosures are initiated between the concept and design phase and completed after the build phase. Concepts are initially disclosed between the concept and design phase, usually with the filing of a provisional patent application. Disclosure is usually completed and full patent application is filed between the build and launch phases after additional testing and refinement has been completed.

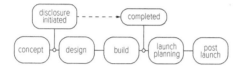

05 What is the process for approving an employee(s) invention for patent filing?

Department employees bring invention ideas to regularly scheduled department meetings, from there ideas are passed to inside counsel for cursory review of patentability and then are sent to c-level IP strategy meeting to determine how the concept may with overall patent strategy, Concepts vetted for patenting are then referred back down to the inventor for patent disclosure, concepts not patented may be kept as trade secrets or defensively disclosed.

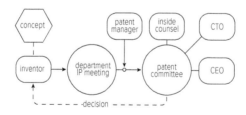

Report prepared by TurboPatent Corporation using TurboPatent® Analytics

06

What is the process for assuring company ownership of the invention (inventor assignment)?

Company ownership of inventions is addressed in the employee handbook and in employee employment contracts and contractor contracts. Employees cede rights to intellectual property relating to the subject matter of the employee's employment and which is developed while employee is employed at the company. An annual review is conducted to ensure that valid assignment agreements are on file for every patent.

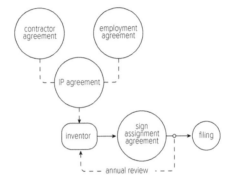

164

07

What is the process for legally protecting the company during technical disclosures from 3rd parties?

NDA's and UnDA's are used to legally protect the company during technical disclosures from 3rd parties. Inside counsel makes assesment of which type to use based on relationship and current legal agreements with the 3rd party.

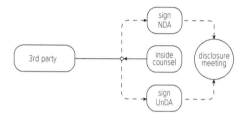

08

What is done with employee invention submissions that are not approved to be patented?

Employee invention submissions which are not protected by patent or trade secret are defensively disclosed to protect against patenting by other entities.

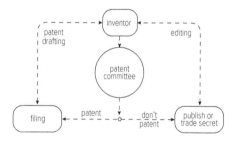

09 What are the goals and processes for cutting patents from the Company's patent portfolio?

Goals for pruning patents from the company patent portfolio are to maintain the revenue generation ability of the portfolio. As such, patents are valuated anually. Strategic value as well as dollar value are assessed during valuation of IP. Patents whose revenue is outstripped by the cost of maintenance are evaluated for potential pruning. A patent earmarked for pruning is abandoned if a buyer cannot be found within a year.

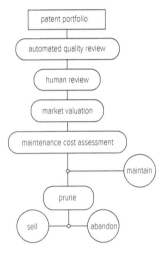

10 Does the company use outside counsel to prepare and prosecute its patents and prepare its trade secrets?
   a. Percentage inside counsel prosecution vs outside counsel prosecution?

Patent prosecution performed by outside counsel - 85%
Trade secret preparation performed by outside counsel - 2%

Percentage of prosecution performed by
outside counsel

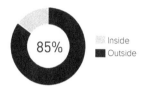

Percentage of trade secret preparation
performed by outside counsel

Report prepared by TurboPatent Corporation using TurboPatent® Analytics

11 What business terms does the company use with legal counsel?
a. Percent internal patent attorney/agent cost?
b. Percent fixed fee or capped fee structure?
c. Percent hourly fee.

Outside counsel are almost entirely retained on a fixed-fee basis, with only a fraction retained on an hourly basis for consulting on specific trade secret related issues.

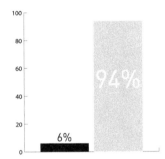

12 Is there a legally compliant system in place for protecting company trade-secrets?

Inventions marked for trade secret protection are forwarded to inside counsel. Inside counsel writes a trade secret "disclosure" where the invention is described in sufficient detail to allow for patentability, but is maintained in an internal database with restricted access.

168

Cultural Audit

01

Has the CEO contributed as an inventor to one or more patent application in the last two years?
a. Inventive contributors on the BOD?
b. Inventive contributors on the Executive Management Team?

During the past two years, the CEO has been named as an inventor in 2 patent applications. On the board of directors, the CTO has been named as an inventor in 10 patent applications within the last two years. Inventive contributions by the executive management team varies by divisions VP of Research and development has been named as an inventor in 8 applications, while the VP of sales and marketing has been named in 3 applications.

Company CEO

2

invention
submissions

| Industry Leader | 5 |
| Industry Average | 0.2 |

Company CTO

10

invention
submissions

| Industry Leader | 22 |
| Industry Average | 4.3 |

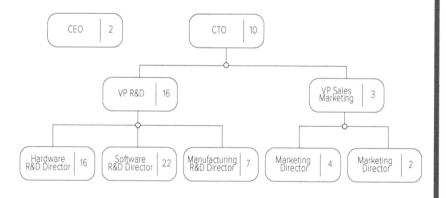

32   Report prepared by TurboPatent Corporation using TurboPatent® Analytics

Who are the top 5 inventors in each division of your company?

The top five inventors by division

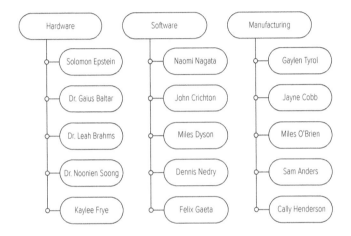

Hardware	Software	Manufacturing
Solomon Epstein	Naomi Nagata	Gaylen Tyrol
Dr. Gaius Baltar	John Crichton	Jayne Cobb
Dr. Leah Brahms	Miles Dyson	Miles O'Brien
Dr. Noonien Soong	Dennis Nedry	Sam Anders
Kaylee Frye	Felix Gaeta	Cally Henderson

03 Do the company's hiring practices include a review and measurement of the new hire's past demonstration of inventiveness

Company's includes personal background questions for applicants to gauge their inventiveness and familiarity with the patent process.

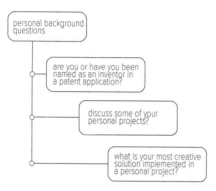

04 Does the company's employee review process monitor and recognize invention?

Company's employee review process tracks personal projects and offers patentability evaluation of the project during its developments.

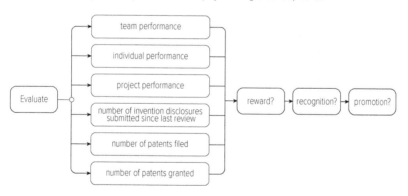

Report prepared by TurboPatent Corporation using TurboPatent® Analytics

05

Does the company utilize reward and recognition programs?
a. How do these programs compare to your competitors?
b. What is the employee participation level in these programs?

Company's reward and recognition program offers provides greater benefits for participating employees relative to the industry average. Although the program is beter than the industry average, employee participation varies by division and is lower than industry averages participation reates hardware and marketing divisions.

06 What is the research and development organization's attitude toward patents?
a. Enthusiastic about participating as inventors.
b. Understands its good business practice and a necessary component to the company's success in the market.
c. Neutral
d. Generally not interested in the process...believe it's a waste of time
e. Philosophically opposed to patents and unwilling to contribute.

Company gauges the organizational attitude towards patents through a survey offered to employees in the R&D divisions. Survey questions mirror questions found in an blind industry survey conducted by a third party organization.

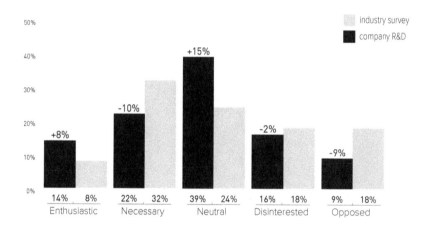

Report prepared by TurboPatent Corporation using TurboPatent® Analytics

Does the company use "Open Invention" techniques in developing IP?
a. If yes, describe the program both qualitatively and quantitatively.

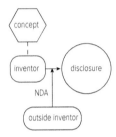

What did this report tell you about where your company stands regarding IP management? In our experience, it's rare for an organization to ask many of the questions contained in the report, let alone have a firm grasp on the answers. It's clearly very important and useful information, so why isn't it regularly reported? Because without automation, it's a massive task to obtain and maintain the information. Also, no one is asking.

That in itself should be a warning.

You are probably asking yourself right now: How come none of my IP people gathered that information? How come they didn't know this stuff already? How vulnerable have I left my company by not investigating this earlier?

Recognition of weakness is the first step to a solution. If nothing else, you now know what you don't know. And these unknowns are likely your greatest vulnerabilities when it comes to threats from competitors and trolls. Your first order of business is to identify the holes in your knowledge base regarding your company's IP operations. The second is to determine what you need to do to fill those holes—that is, what new systems and employees need to be put in place to make sure the necessary information is systematically gathered.

The bottom line: Your company must be able to provide the required information in this IP Audit. Only then can you fully execute a successful IP strategy that will keep you competitive in a changing marketplace, now and in the years to come.

We're not done, though. The IP audit is just Step One. It's important and necessary—but it is also insufficient. To extract real benefit, you've still got some fine-tuning to do.

The best way to do this is to revisit your audit answers and ask yourself the following questions:

1. Quality
   - How good is your patent portfolio?
   - How does it fulfill the company's goals in terms of both operational IP (which makes your company more competitive) and functional IP (which protects you from outside threats)?
   - What would the perfect portfolio look like?
   - Do you have the right professionals to get you there?

2. Execution
   - How well does your company use its IP?
   - Is IP part of your business strategy or just a backup defense?
   - Does your senior team understand the role of IP and incorporate it into their planning?
   - Are you generating enough new IP to replace old patents and maintain your competitive position?
   - Is your IP generating all of the revenues that it should, either directly or indirectly?

3. Culture
   - Does everyone in your company—from the Executive Row to the labs to marketing and sales—have a pro-IP attitude, one that is always looking for opportunities to take new ideas and turn them into protected inventions?
   - Are they dedicated to seeing those ideas become revenue-producing products and services?
   - Do you reinforce that culture with your leadership, along with a system of rewards and recognition?
   - Are you prepared to do whatever it takes to make your company an industry-leading innovator?

Don't worry if you can't answer all of these questions in the affirmative just yet. The rest of this book is dedicated to telling you how to get there.

> **The CEO Patent Report is the perfect starting point for establishing both a vision and a plan for Inventioneering your way to leadership company performance.**

Chapter 11

Inventioneering

As noted in Chapter 2, W. Edwards Deming's work proved that a focus on Quality First is the best way to achieve not just the highest quality, but improved overall efficiency as well.

But there is a second Deming rule: Everything you desire to improve must be monitored and measured. As you can imagine, upholding this second rule can be challenging when it comes to inventions and patents. For example, a great invention does not guarantee a great patent. It is only the start.

Why doesn't a great invention guarantee a great patent? Because in addition to being an inventive concept in the mind of the inventor, a great patent must also:

- faithfully capture the inventive concept and successfully and accurately be prosecuted to the full expanse of the inventive concept;
- have excellent technical quality—that is, be sufficiently well written so that it survives tests of validity;
- have its essence proven to be something the market has embraced, so much so that your company and even your competitors generate significant revenues from products or services that depend upon the invention.

Fulfilling these steps using traditional approaches can be time and cost prohibitive. Fortunately, Inventioneering embraces new technological solutions that allow a company to assess the quality and efficiency for each of these aspects of invention and patents.

We have used the term Inventioneering a lot in this book. But let's now get very specific: What exactly is Inventioneering?

Let's start at the end and work backwards:

- Inventioneering results in the creation of higher-quality inventions and patents, more inventions and patents, and IP created or acquired more efficiently (i.e., at lower cost).
- Inventioneering uses best practices, from the top of the organization to the bottom, and from the outset of every project lifecycle to the end.
- Inventioneering is first and foremost the creation of a company culture that inculcates into all of its employees the notion that inventing and protecting inventions are at the core of the value of the company itself, and everyone in the company must help with this mission.

To give you a sense of how deeply Inventioneering should be embedded into an organization to maximize the benefits, here's an analogy: We worked with an extremely successful Fortune 100 company that has embedded into its very DNA a belief that a key competitive differentiator is the systematic use of large data sets to make decisions at every level of the company. Indeed, the importance of data analytics is written in that company's employee handbook; any potential new hire's inclination to embrace this culture or not is a significant criteria for whether or not they'll be hired. Big Data is the basis of every decision, strategic or tactical. The company also applies these same rules to its invention process and patents.

This culture of data analytics did not arise haphazardly. Rather, it was the result of a conscious and purposeful effort that started at the very top of the company and was driven home daily throughout the operation. The use of Big Data was, and is, continuously monitored and measured. Anyone who endeavors to succeed within this organization—or even just to remain employed—must quickly become data-driven.

No doubt there are aspects of your enterprise that are truly embedded into your culture. But is a commitment to invention as pervasive in your company as it should be?

The remainder of this chapter will outline strategies to embed Inventioneering into your company culture. It is not something that will happen overnight. But you may well be surprised at how quickly you and your team can use it to instill change.

Inventioneering Goals: The 10 Plan – Year One

The Inventioneering "10 Plan" is a set of goals that are realistic for any company that is committed to Inventioneering. As you saw in Chapter 10, with the right systems in place, an organization can monitor and measure progress in achieving its Inventioneering goals.

Ten goals for a first-year investment in Inventioneering:

1. Increase the number of inventive contributors (more on this in the next chapter) by 10 percent, one of which must be the CEO.
2. Increase the annual number of invention disclosures by 10 percent.
3. Increase the annual number of patent filings by 10 percent. These filings should adhere to Inventioneering

quality standards, which we'll discuss more later.

4. Decrease the patent drafting time and the cost of drafting and prosecution by 10 percent.
5. Replace 10 percent of your outside patent counsel (see the CEO Report in Chapter 10), starting with the poorest performers in terms of patent quality output.
6. Abandon 10 percent of your lowest quality and least valuable pending and granted patents.
7. Hire ten new employees (number can be adjusted based on company size), each with ten or more verifiable inventions.
8. Require each new major project to produce a list of ten or more inventions that might differentiate the proposed product or service in the market. Require the project lead (not the patent counsel) to present this list in the project funding approval process.
9. File ten or more patents that directly target your major competitors' IP in emerging markets. Don't worry if your company has no intention of building a product including said invention.
10. Publicize at least ten inventive contributions and their importance to the company.

Now, here is the punchline: **These goals should not be exclusive to your chief IP counsel** (or whatever title you use). Assign them to the heads of your operating groups, and ensure your chief IP counsel and his or her team play a major support role in achieving these goals, as well as in verifying the quality of the final work product.

Your head of R&D, your head of product development, and even your sales and marketing chiefs should own their share of these goals. All too often, we see the patent practitioners and patent managers who are charged with the organization's invention goals struggle to get the attention of the inventors.

The result is often worthless inventions that have little resemblance to the technology being innovated. The inventor thinks it is his or her job just to engineer or science the hell out of something—which, after reading this book, you now know is only part of the job. In actuality, Inventioneering is an inventor's job, and nothing short of that is acceptable. Company-wide Inventioneering is critical to success. If the responsibility, the goals, the time and the attention to accomplish those goals do not flow down to the inventors, your company will continue to pay a lot of money for junk. This is the CEO's job to fix, so fix it.

Inventioneering Funding & Budgeting

But where does the money come from to fund the Inventioneering 10 Plan?

No funding is needed. By embedding Inventioneering in the company culture, focusing on measurable quality output and implementing your version of the 10 Plan, your corporate expenditure on patents will decline. Unless, of course, you choose to invest the savings in doing more or going faster, or even both.

By taking advantage of technological advances and best practices in the creation and assessment of your IP, your company will have the data and processes to enable more rigor and discipline to be applied to current (low) quality and (high) expenditures. Undoubtedly, your existing granted patent portfolio is riddled with worthless junk that costs millions of dollars annually in maintenance fees alone. The years of costly prosecution of your applications that too often result in invalid or valueless assets will now be monitored and the waste eliminated, which will mean millions of additional dollars in savings. And the traditional, bespoke methods of creating inventions and patent applications will be upgraded to use modern computer-aided development and analysis tools, also resulting in significant quality improvements and cost savings.

As for budgeting, we've already discussed the several methods used to conduct IP budgeting in corporations today. Most companies maintain IP creation and acquisition as a separate expenditure in a distinct organization. They typically conduct a comparison to last year's budget and then put some small percent increase in place—and maybe even take a look at what they think their competitors might be doing. These, however, are suboptimal hand waves thrown out at the expense of the real task of allocating financial resources to this critical component of the company.

We believe you should, at a minimum, tie IP budgeting to your company's R&D financial plan. Once Inventioneering is embedded within your company, you will likely spend less on IP than your competition does—assuming they are using legacy methods—and yet you will still create as much, if not more, valuable IP.

That said, we also recommend increasing your IP budget. We have taken great pains throughout this book to show you that your company is facing severe, even existential, IP threats on multiple fronts. Now is that point in history when those who step hard on the IP accelerator by investing more in patents and embedding the very best systems and practices into their cultures will emerge victorious. Simply put, it's time for a lead foot.

Inventioneering Strategy

In the CEO Report included in Chapter 10, we categorized six levels of IP strategy:

1. Reactive Patent Strategy
2. Defensive Patent Strategy
3. Offensive Patent Strategy
4. Revenue Patent Strategy
5. Aligned Patent Strategy
6. Inventioneering Strategy

The Inventioneering Strategy embraces and extends levels 2 through 5.

Practicing a Reactive Patent Strategy (No. 1) means you do nothing except react after the fact to a lawsuit or a threat. In reality, it is practicing no strategy at all, and yet we see it often. Why is this? In some cases it's the executive team ignoring what it doesn't understand or, almost as bad, simply doing what has been done before. In other cases, the excuse is one of budget, such as, "We can't afford the patent strategy we would like to have." This is a bad answer to a false choice. The Reactive Strategy may save money in the very short term but will cost many multiples of the savings and potential earnings when the day of reckoning eventually comes.

Perhaps the most common reason for employing a Reactive Patent Strategy is that the people entrusted with advising the leadership team are not up to the task. In some instances, they lack vision or skills; other times they don't have enough visibility or authority. The truth is that someone, maybe several people, should be fired, be they incompetent advisors or the people getting in the way of a more proactive strategy. Simply put, following a Reactive Patent Strategy is a bad practice, one that increases risk and liability—including to the board of directors—while decreasing the opportunity for higher margins and revenues.

The next four strategies (No. 2 to No. 5), are essentially dead ends as well; at best, they are half measures.

By comparison, the Inventioneering Strategy offers the only complete—and completely successful—strategy. As such, it should be set within the context of the company's overall strategy and business goals. A foundational goal, of course, is always the freedom to operate your business. (In case you need a reminder why, think back to the chilling effect patent legal activity had on RIM's ability to function, as outlined in Chapter 4.) Protecting the company's core business by creating patents or trade secrets where key inventions are concerned is fundamental to the defensive aspect of Inventioneering strategy. Selectively encircling key competitors with blocking patents will strengthen your company's defensive position with bargaining chips should those competitors attempt to inhibit your company from operating its core business. Trolls or non-practicing entities are other actors who might impinge on your ability to run your business. The most effective strategies for countering NPEs include participating in a patent defense network and/or buying patent litigation insurance from an organization such as RPX Corporation.

The good news is that in 2014 the Supreme Court significantly lowered the standard by which litigating parties of a weak patent case could be held accountable for the defendant's legal fees (Octane Fitness, LLC v. ICON Health & Fitness, Inc.). In the past, judges had been reluctant to rule that litigants must pay defendants' fees. Now, in order for a judge to rule that a litigant must pay the defendant's fees, the court only requires the defendant to show that the case is weak relative to normal patent cases. This outcome is referred to as "fee shifting," and has put a lot more at risk for those who would file frivolous patent suits. In short, it is an excellent counter threat to those practicing troll behavior.

You must also vigorously defend against spurious assertions of infringement. Negotiate and license if your company clearly infringes a valid patent claim. However, paying off tenacious trolls, even at a very low dollar amount, when your products do not infringe on the IP they are asserting (and/or if the patent they are asserting is invalid) is not a good idea. While a payout may initially seem like smart business, over the long term it is anything but. More likely it will make you an ongoing target and end up costing you more.

The Inventioneering Strategy requires the determination to employ an offensive component on a case-by-case basis. While you have a fiduciary responsibility to enforce your patents where infringement is harming your business, the process is more complex than simply filing suit against every company impinging on some part of your IP.

The truth about large corporations, including yours, is that all are infringing on some part of someone else's IP. Given that maintaining freedom to operate is tantamount, you want to consider the consequences carefully before you start a fight that threatens that freedom. Proactive infringement assertions are best targeted at blatant copycats that have invested little in their own innovation efforts and are simply leeching off your company's good work. It is important that you send a clear message to flagrant abusers of your IP.

Shareholders are increasingly requiring management teams and BODs to optimize the investments made in their patent portfolios. Many large companies are using their portfolios to generate significant income streams. IBM, Oracle and Microsoft, to name a few, generate billions of dollars in patent licensing revenue. The creation and acquisition of patents are sunk costs and the overhead to monetize patents relative to the revenue generated is low. As a result the margins are huge. One billion dollars in IP licensing income can yield the same profit as $5 billion to $10 billion in product or service revenue. These are serious earnings that can have a material effect on your company's stock price, so it's no wonder investors are holding you to the task.

However, there are risks to this strategy. Creating or acquiring IP for the primary purpose of monetization can distract your company from its primary purpose of creating amazing products and services for your customers. Prosecuting your own company's inventions for the purpose of licensing can have an adverse effect on what should be the more important effort of creating quality patents that protect your core business.

For all these reasons, the Inventioneering Strategy is to first build a portfolio that protects your core business and your freedom to operate. Only then should you look for licensing opportunities within those bounds. Having a deft licensing group that understands these complexities and the greater corporate well-being is very important. Once your company has an overall patent advantage, you can negotiate a favorable deal (usually one that includes revenue and a cross license). This simultaneously generates profits for your bottom line and reduces the risk of future litigation.

Another creative approach we have seen is a corporation providing IP licenses to earlier stage companies for future royalty revenue streams or in exchange for equity in the startup company. It's a bit like a university tech transfer office using its patents as a way to place a bet on a new venture without having to pay any of the product development or company operational costs.

Again, your Inventioneering Strategy must align with your corporate goals and should be deployed throughout the organization. Moreover, it must reach into the future.

Your company is sub-optimized if you are only protecting impending products and services. Invention is a form of predicting and then developing the future. As a result, your company should have an outlook on what that future is and how your company is going to dominate it.

To that end, your Inventioneering Strategy must include the investment and use of human resources to explore beyond your current product roadmaps. As former Sun Microsystems CTO Bill Joy famously said, "No matter who you are, most of the smartest people work for someone else." Which means you must look outside your company to invent your best future. In addition, your Inventioneering Strategy should be keyed towards open innovation, both in its creation and its distribution.

We will talk more about the process of implementing your Inventioneering Strategy in the remaining chapters.

> In the mid-1990s, while starting a company focused on using the then new Internet to supply "online learning," we observed that Nordstrom, a Seattle-headquartered department store, had remarkable employees.

Chapter 12

Inventioneers

Nordstrom's employees were universally friendly and helpful professionals ready to serve their customers. Our assumption was that Nordstrom must have some amazing training programs and we wanted to "bottle" its method into our online learning system.

We were able to schedule a meeting with the woman responsible for new-employee orientation and training. When we dove into our questions about Nordstrom's magical training content and delivery, however, we were met with a puzzled look. The training executive didn't seem to believe there was anything different about Nordstrom's approach compared to those of past employers where she had managed training.

How was it possible that Nordstrom could have such consistently great employees without a special training "sauce"? It just didn't add up. Serendipitously, after talking a while longer, we stumbled upon the topic of recruiting and hiring practices. And there we discovered what enabled Nordstrom to deliver such amazing service: It hired great people. Nordstrom expended great effort in finding just the right people whose profiles and personalities were ideal for delivering wonderful customer service.

Types of Inventioneers

This same philosophy should be applied when hiring Inventioneers. We suspect your company is populated with people who embody a range of profiles and skills. And while most will adapt well to Inventioneering, others may not. They may no longer fit within the new culture you are creating.

Going forward, however, you should make sure that you are hiring people who do fit into your Inventioneering culture. As it turns out, there is a little-known but easily accessed resource to assist in this effort—a sort of "LinkedIn for inventors"—called the USPTO database, and it is freely available to the public. It is estimated that there are about 10 million corporate inventors (engineers, scientists and others) worldwide who have been named an inventor on a patent application filed by a company, and each and every one of them can be found within the database.

Let's say your company is about to embark on a project relating to automotive battery technology. It is relatively easy to do a search on the USPTO database and find the names and locations of incredibly smart people who have proven themselves in this technology. Your people also can read and evaluate their patent applications to gain insight into the knowledge base and skills of these potential employees.

The use of this resource and the targeting of named inventors should become a key part of your company's hiring requirements and practices.

People listed as inventors on patents only represent one type of Inventioneer, however. According to patent law, you must be listed on a patent as an inventor if you have contributed to one or more of the patent claims in the application. The law also states that you may not be listed as an inventor on the patent application if you did not contribute to one or more of the claims.

Most often, the inventors listed on a patent application are engineers or scientists of some sort. These people have figured out a creative, useful, new and non-obvious way to provide value. What they dreamed up solved some problem—and perhaps embodied some general vision—brought forward by others. Those other people, the ones who brought the problem to light, while not technically or legally named as inventors on the patent, are also Inventioneers and are critical to Inventioneering. In fact, they embody it.

Which is why we divide Inventioneers up into three groups. Keep in mind that the following groups are loosely defined, as crossover is both frequent and highly encouraged:

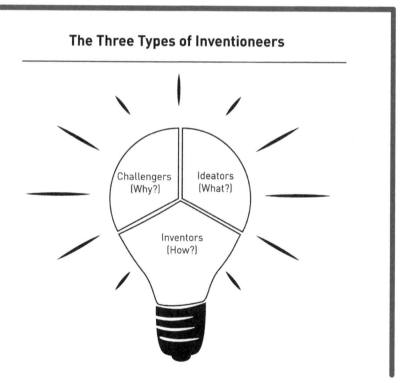

The Three Types of Inventioneers

Challengers (Why?)

Ideators (What?)

Inventors (How?)

Challengers

Challengers can and should be almost everyone in your company, including you. A Challenger observes a problem or gap and perceives the value in solving that problem or filling that gap. In short, a Challenger is someone with the answer to the question "Why?"

A Challenger is good at observing difficulties customers might be having with current products or services, or gaps in your offerings. Salespeople, customer service agents, production people and repair technicians are in great positions to see these customer issues and product gaps. The problem is that these are also the people rarely included in invention discussions. That is a mistake. Find ways to bring them in to the conversation.

We cannot emphasize enough the importance of thoroughly understanding the customer or market problem. It is common practice that during strategy sessions or brainstorming the group budgets about 10 percent of its time to discussing the problem and the remainder of the time on possible solutions. Simply put, that is wrong.

The group, in fact, needs to research and explore the problem both deeply and broadly. Why will the market care? What is the pain that needs to be relieved? Challengers have the answers to these questions. Empowering these people in a systematic way to participate and contribute to the company's inventive process will make your IP portfolio more valuable. At the same time, it will move your culture toward Inventioneering, toward a culture that does not produce worthless patents.

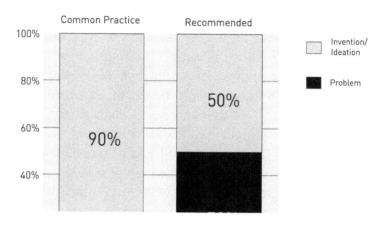

Common Practice vs Recommended Time Split

Common Practice   Recommended

Invention/
Ideation

Problem

100%

80%

60%

40%

50%

90%

Commonly, too little time is spent focused on dissecting the problem, while much time is devoted to brainstorming possible solutions. For better results, it is recommended that a greater proportion of time be spent more deeply analyzing and understanding the problem.

Ideators

Often referred to as visionaries, Ideators are people who see the big picture. They are usually information collectors and are good at synthesizing information from unrelated fields. They have great imaginations and are sometimes seen as dreamers. Apple's founder Steve Jobs is an example of an iconic Ideator.

Playing the Ideator role in Inventioneering requires a person partake in a creative process, sometimes alone and with no particular schedule. That said, the results are usually better when Ideators are part of a small and diverse group. With the problem well understood by all, the task of the Ideator is to generate, develop and communicate new ideas that solve the pain identified by the Challenger.

Inventors

Inventors are usually those with some quantum of science and engineering skills. Their role is to come up with answers for how the high-level ideas proposed by Ideators can be built so that they actually do solve problems and fill in gaps. In turn, those who contribute as Inventors are the ones named as inventors on the patent application. Note, however, that when it comes to filing a patent, the Inventors do not actually have to build anything, but they do need to show how they would build it, and share their best approach. The majority of the highest valued patents are those that describe a novel way to build something that might not actually be built for years to come.

In the words of hockey great Wayne Gretzky, the best Inventors "skate to where the puck is going to be, not where it has been." (Gretzky's wisdom applies to Challengers as well.) Projecting technology trends onto your planned products and services will yield the most valuable IP. And remember, you don't need to build it today.

Inventors also check for sanity. For instance, a great solution to the problem of poor gas mileage might be to create a transportation machine that produces more energy than it consumes. That would be fantastic but, unfortunately, it is impossible: perpetual motion machines defy the laws of physics. (On a side note: perpetual motion machines have been officially declared un-patentable in order to save the USPTO from having to deal with crackpots.)

One more point about Inventioneers: Challengers, Ideators and Inventors do not have to be employees. Here, as elsewhere throughout your business, the concept of Open Innovation applies. Adding talented outside parties to the mix is very effective when it comes to Inventioneering.

At our company, we bring in a diverse group of Ideators and Inventors from outside of the organization, which we call the iSquad (the "i" stands for invention). We currently work with a company that, as a matter of practice, publishes challenges to a host of external experts in a given field of science or technology (maintaining confidentially, of course). It is the equivalent of a Request for Proposal (RFP) that might be submitted to vendors for delivering services to the company, except that in this case the external experts receive a Request for Invention (RFI). Based on the responses, the company hosts an Inventioneering session, bringing in several of the outside inventors to work directly with company employees.

Using an iSquad, as we call it, to create defensive patent assets as part of a competitor blocking strategy is a good idea. Composed of people with specific knowledge of the target technology sector, the iSquad model offers a win-win scenario. It doesn't disrupt your company's own efforts at creating better products and services for your customers, and the enterprise avoids long-term employee costs. Of course, patent ownership, confidentiality and other legal matters must be carefully documented. But the benefits of having an iSquad far outweigh the costs of the paperwork involved.

> Inventioneering depends on replacing many legacy aspects of human-centered systems dedicated to the creation and assessment of IP with a machine-centered approach. In fact, we have an instantiation of such a device—a patent machine—in our own company, which we call the TurboPatent Machine™. We expect to see an increasing amount of technology applied throughout the industry and, as a result, an increase in the number of patent machines.

Chapter 13

Patent Machines and Secure Systems

Artificial intelligence comprised of natural language processing (e.g., IBM's Watson), machine learning (IBM's Deep Blue) and big data analytics (Wall Street trading systems) has surpassed the trained professional's ability to operate at the center of the corporate patent process. As an example, the CEO report shown in Chapter 10 is, in fact, a computer-compiled executive summary representing more than fifty thousand pages of machine-generated analytics—all of it instantaneously available to the reader. By comparison, a well-trained patent professional would require a minimum of 2.4 hours per patent to produce a similar report (see math below).

The Math

$$\left(2.4\,\text{hours} \times 5{,}000\,\text{patents} \right) = 12{,}000\,\text{hours} \times \$250/\text{hour} = \$3\,\text{Million}$$

Traditional methods of analyzing patent portfolios are prohibitively expensive!

Not only would the traditional approach cost $3 million at an hourly rate of $250 (a low rate for an experienced patent professional), but it would also take approximately a hundred attorneys nearly a month to generate the report. Even worse, the legacy approach would be riddled with errors and inconsistencies, not to mention difficult for the client to instantly access. By comparison, a patent machine would conduct the same research in just a few hours—and, as we'll discuss more below, without the errors and inconsistencies.

Until now, thanks to time and cost justifications, corporations had plausible deniability about the state of their patent portfolios. This is no longer true. Just as chess masters can no longer compete with a chess computer, patent practitioners can no longer compete with a patent machine. But that doesn't mean they are ready to acknowledge that new reality. The world of IP management is largely populated with attorneys and other legal professionals, a conservative group notorious for its glacial adoption of new technology. What that means is that your company cannot wait for these folks to lead it through this transformation. Leadership must come from you.

A patent machine isn't limited to the task of analyzing granted and pending patents. It can also be applied to all aspects of patent quality assurance, including assessing inventive concepts, reporting on the quality of a drafted application and monitoring the horrible things that can happen during the prosecution phase of the corporation's new crown jewels.

Quality ...

$$Quality = \frac{Results\ of\ work\ efforts}{Total\ costs}$$

Using a patent machine, automated quality checks can (and should) be applied throughout the patent process.

And that's not all. A patent machine can take input directly from the inventor during the product development process and produce a high quality patent application, responding intelligently and effectively to all office actions during prosecution. In addition, a patent machine has the advantage of being able to access millions of statistics and patterns not comprehensible to the human mind.

When the application is allowed, a patent machine can then proofread the final documents to make sure the USPTO did not make any errors—which at this stage it does more than 50 percent of the time. Humans get tired and they make mistakes; machines don't. According to cognitive scientists, most humans would tell you that there are three Fs in the sentence below, even after reviewing it multiple times.

Finished files are the result of years of scientific study combined with the experience of years . . .

But a machine will always tell you that there are six, which is correct. In a study, less than 10 percent of educated people produced the right answer.

Security

An issue that looms large for corporations and their IP is theft, especially when it comes to new ideas that are not yet protected by a patent filing. This has become a very serious concern, particularly now that we know that the Chinese government is sponsoring the theft of American corporations' inventions and trade secrets.

It has been proved that the function of the People's Liberation Army's notorious Unit 61398 is to hack Western databases. Specific attacks are designed to steal large volumes of intellectual property, predominantly from innovative nations like the United States of America. In other words, from you. So, more than ever, you need to defend yourself.

As you fully understand by now, IP is your most valuable asset and it is highly coveted by your competitors. Surprisingly, most inventions travel through extremely insecure routes prior to being protected as a filed patent application. Patent processing involves numerous documents, drafts and reviews, as well as frequent communications with a wide range of parties. There are many potential attack vectors in the complicated data flow that comprises the common corporate patent practice when using outside patent counsel (as depicted in the diagram at right).

As a result, legal entities are particularly attractive to attackers. In its 2015 Annual Security Report, for example, Cisco Systems, Inc. ranked law firms as the seventh most vulnerable industry to cyberattacks. And Mandiant, a cybersecurity firm, recently reported that at least eighty of the one hundred largest American law firms had suffered some type of malicious computer breach.

Small to mid-sized legal firms typically do not have hardened computer environments or full-time security operations personnel. Additionally, it is a common in the legal industry for employees to work remotely, either from home or from a variety of public locations. As a result, intellectual property is regularly stored on portable devices, which may or may not be adequately protected, monitored and recorded.

Furthermore, legal entities almost never publicly disclose security breaches, despite the sensitivity of the information that may be exposed. This is unfortunate but understandable, as there are few legal requirements for law firms to disclose breaches, unlike banks and retailers, which are held accountable by strict breach notification laws.

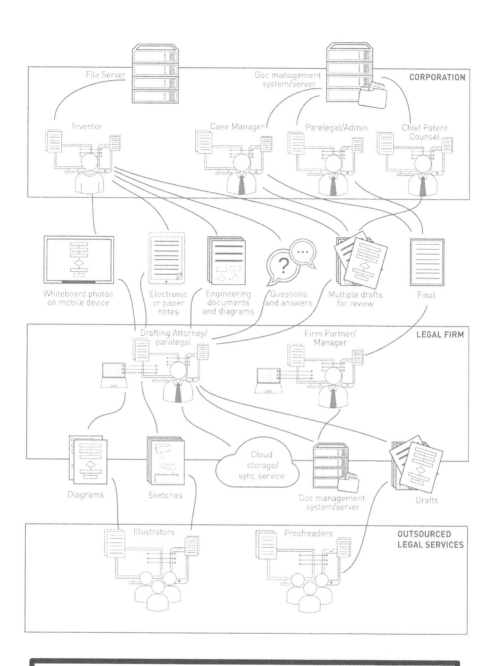

File Server

Doc management
system/server

CORPORATION

Inventor

Case Manager

Parelegal/Admin

Chief Patent
Counsel

Whiteboard photos
on mobile device

Electronic
or paper
notes

Engineering
documents
and diagrams

Questions
and answers

Multiple drafts
for review

Final

Drafting Attorney/
paralegal

Firm Partner/
Manager

LEGAL FIRM

Diagrams

Sketches

Cloud
storage/
sync service

Doc management
system/server

Drafts

Illustrators

Proofreaders

OUTSOURCED
LEGAL SERVICES

This visual shows the many potential attack points in the complicated data flow that comprises the common corporate patent practice and traditional methods of patent production.

Beyond the possible areas of attack during the patent drafting and prosecution process, there is also the issue of sensitive communication being discovered during a patent's litigation. With so many devices storing various drafts of patent applications—and the communication surrounding those drafts—it is difficult to purge potentially sensitive information that could invalidate a granted patent. During the typical multi-year patent creation and prosecution process, sensitive data can inadvertently be spread to a wide variety of individuals, devices and networks, as well as other locations—any of which could have poor security controls. Even worse, data backup and redundancy systems are unlikely to be purged of sensitive and potentially harmful data.

Happily, security and data management are fundamental pillars for top-tier cloud storage providers, which invest millions of dollars in security technologies and expertise to protect the billions they have at risk. It is, after all, their business. No private organization can afford such heavy investment in security, largely because it is not their primary business.

That means that the secure creation and management of patents is an application that benefits greatly from cloud computing. The convoluted, tedious and highly vulnerable traditional processes are transformed into a powerful, globally accessible, easily tracked and far more secure cloud-based system. The most current version of documents can be viewed and edited on multiple devices, all the while staying secure in a cloud locker. Comments and communication can all be made within the cloud application and eliminated when appropriate. Such a cloud-based system is shown in the image right. Note the radical reduction in the "spaghetti" of communication connections.

Ironically, the legal sector has been one most resistant to the use of cloud computing as a solution to the security and data management issues that plague it. This is a very real problem that exists now. Once again, it will take the leadership of the CEO to demand that the processes used to create and protect a company's most valuable asset be secured. Don't wait: demand that security now. If your outside legal support refuses, or even prevaricates, hire a firm that will do what you ask. Today.

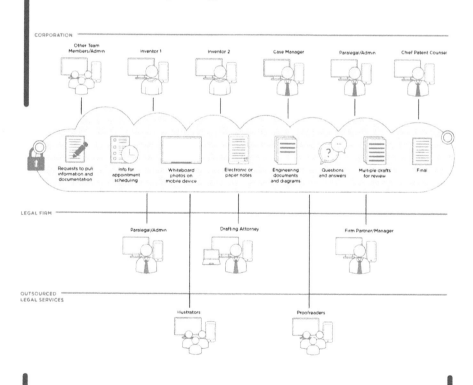

Cloud computing enables the secure creation and management of patents. The number of potential attack vectors is decreased greatly in this model as compared to the traditional methods of producing patents.

As we near the end of this book, we offer a playbook for embedding a repeatable and sustainable organizational system that will deliver on your stated IP goals—with patent quality underlying each of those goals.

Chapter 14

Inventioneering Process, Part 1

The overriding tenets of the Inventioneering process are:

1. Inventioneering is directed, modeled, recognized and rewarded by an organization's top executives.
2. Invention capture is a required component and happens simultaneously with the development of any new product/service or the development of enhancements to an existing product/service.
3. The primary parties responsible for process and goal attainment are the line managers (the legal department acts as support).
4. Invention review and filing happens rapidly ("first to file") and prosecution review happens with each correspondence with the patent office.
5. Quality – defined as a complete and accurate representation of the invention, crisply defined, valid and defensible—is the highest priority.
6. IP training and patent automation are embraced throughout the organization.
7. Measurement – the monitoring of appropriate elements at each stage of the patent process, quarterly reports and annual audits—is performed and the

results yield measurable consequences (positive and negative) that can be converted into actionable items.

We will assume, for the purposes of this chapter, that your company's annual IP audit has already taken place, and that your IP goals and strategy are set. An employee IP training program has also been deployed and a patent recognition and reward plan has been instituted. Hiring practices now include filters that help identify people who embody the skills of great challengers, visionaries and inventors. Patent automation tools for invention capture and patent creation and assessment have also been selected and deployed. We further assume that you have now used those automated tools to "prune" or repair flawed assets in your current portfolio, and to identify and remove the least effective practitioners.

With the above in place we now will move on to the five major process steps in your Inventioneering practice. Underlying each of these steps are the automated systems and ongoing support processes that, when combined, yield Inventioneering:

Foundation for Invention

Invention Creation/Capture	Triage	Draft	Prosecute	Portfolio Management

Automated Tools	Employee Training	Hiring	Recognize & Reward	Measure

Inventioneering combines the five major process steps in the invention practice with underlying automated systems and ongoing support processes.

Our goal at this point is to give you the right level of depth within each of these procedural steps, understanding that your Inventioneering team will provide the further detail required for those working the day-to-day tactics.

Invention Creation and Capture

Modern research and product development organizations are highly skilled at finding market gaps that open up an opportunity to create a new product or add a new feature to an existing product or service. Depending upon the methodology—such as Brainstorming, Ideation or TRIZ (not as well known but we highly recommend investigating this approach)—different processes and tools are applied to assist with envisioning creative, novel and useful solutions.

A sampling of the leading companies offering idea management software solutions

Idea Management Software

Innovate	The pioneering platform for cloud-based Innovation Management-from Creative Ideas to Winning Projects
Brightidea	Brightidea enables enterprises to innovate more effectively with the right mix of specialized SaaS software and professional services.
Spigit	#1 innovation management software for crowdsourcing innovation: ideate and collaborate, and implement only the best ideas with Spigit!
Idea Spotlight	Idea Spotlight is a webbased idea management tool that helps businesses of all sizes to uncover, filter and prioritise the best ideas
Ideation 2.0	With 8 years of experience serving companies from all industries and geographies, Qmarkets is a leader in the field of idea management.
Crowdicity	The most flexible and results driven Idea Management platform on the market. Trusted by; LEGO, WWF, John Lewis, The UN, NHS, BBC, P&G
IdeaLab	IdeaLab helps you get real-time feedback, identify problems, find solutions and explore new opportunities.
Codigital	Real time ideas engine. Powerful and engaging way for large groups to generate, prioritize and refine ideas.
Idea Market	Exago's US patented model combines idea management software and expert services to make you achieve sustained innovation results.
Includer	The quickest way to get new ideas and insightful feedback from your team.

Similarly, and depending upon the engineering methodology (e.g., "waterfall" or "agile development"), different processes and tools are applied to envisioning technical approaches that will render a solution to the target problem. The same is true of the next step—that of creating an implementation plan to build the best embodiment of that solution.

These activities can be summarized as:
Problem, Idea, Innovation, Invention

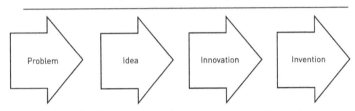

This charts the ordered progression resulting in the creation of invention.

This process occurs thousands of times each day throughout the world. The output of this work is usually one or more of the following: a PowerPoint deck, a product specification, system diagrams, flowcharts, CAD drawings or maybe even a prototype.

All of these outputs are communication instruments used to create a common understanding among all of the stakeholders to the Inventioneering process, including engineers, designers, marketers, salespeople, manufacturing workers and executives. A subsequent patent application is, in fact, simply another form of the same information.

Most often a patent application can and should be created and filed far faster than the actual product can be built. Using a patent machine like that described earlier in this book, an inventor can input the same information he or she is already creating in the engineering and development process—but now that information is used to produce a rough draft of a provisional patent. That draft provisional patent can then be rapidly reviewed and, if approved by your company, quickly completed and filed.

Additionally, the same techniques used to identify worthy problems and novel solutions for the purposes of building products also can be used to anticipate future problems and predict future technologies that will allow for the creation of very valuable IP.

Regularly gathering a cross section of challengers, visionaries and inventors to look into the future and invent solutions to future problems is a powerful method for creating valuable IP for your company. Remember the mental exercise of imagining a competitive business that would put your current company out of business? Have this group pursue that activity, capture the invention that grows from the process and then file patent applications. Even if you choose never to build the products or services that use this patented invention, you have nevertheless created operating freedom and the opportunity to trade or sell this IP down the road.

Measuring the output of your company's invention process is extremely important. It is a proxy of your company's ability to innovate. It is also an indicator of your employees' attitude regarding IP. Growing the number of employee-contributed invention disclosures is a great sign that Inventioneering is being embraced within your organization.

Invention Review and Triage

Not every idea, innovation or invention is worth pursuing. Most large corporations file patents on less than 40 percent of the inventions that their employees bring forward. This can be due to any number of reasons, including budgetary constraints or the invention being dismissed as not patentable. Sometimes inventions aren't pursued because the information provided by the inventor(s) is inadequate or indiscernible; others are ignored because they are thought to add no value to the company.

For all of these reasons, it's essential that your Inventioneering process has a review and triage step for all invention submissions filed with the company. Reviewers assigned to this process will need knowledge of the following: the company's business and product strategy, the technology required to build the invention, the state of the art in the associated technological area, patent and trade secret law, IP licensing and, ideally, what the competition is up to.

Obviously, no one person can be expert in all of these areas. So this critical operation will require a group of individuals with distinct expertise. The group can be organized as a standing committee responsible for the triage of all company inventions, or as a virtual organization led by one individual per technology or business sector.

Committee Approach

This visual represents the "Committee Approach" to Inventioneering.

Either organizational structure requires that the contributors be the best and brightest talent the company can offer. Being selected for participation should be recognized as a substantial honor and rewarded commensurately.

Even though the body of knowledge required is large, if your structure is a standing committee, the group should be small. Jeff Bezos is credited for conceiving the "two pizza" rule: that nothing really great gets done with a group larger than can consume two pizzas at a single meeting. We place that number at somewhere between four and eight people, with the ideal number falling at the lower end of that range.

The virtual approach, which we recommend, assigns an individual to manage the invention and patent process end-to-end for a sector of the company's patents. With this organizational approach, the corporate patent manager (CPM) can draw upon a set of distributed resources across the company for the expertise required to make the triage decision. The CPM operates throughout the entire Inventioneering process for his or her assigned sector, working with the inventors to source invention disclosures, working across the organization to triage the disclosures and taking on the responsibility for the remaining aspects of the Inventioneering process.

A rule of thumb is that a CPM, with good tools, can competently manage about three hundred invention disclosures per year, yielding one hundred patent applications. The time commitment for the patent triage committee should be about one hour for each invention approved for patenting, with the understanding that two to four invention submissions will be reviewed to attain a single green light for moving a submission forward to the patent drafting and filing stage.

It is necessary that the committee be given adequate time to do this vital job well. The time allotment described above is necessary, but that alone is not sufficient. An inevitable problem that exists for both the patent triage committee and the CPM is that the information upon which their opinion is being rendered is sometimes inconsistent and often insufficient.

In non-Inventioneering cultures, inventors often see the CPM and the patent process as a nuisance getting in the way of getting their real jobs done. As a result, the resulting invention disclosures are anywhere from nonexistent to woefully incomplete. Requests for more and better information fall on deaf ears, leaving the CPM or the person responsible for drafting an application to his or her own inventiveness. In these conditions, patent quality inevitably suffers. Even the best patent practitioners and CPMs are not mind readers.

With Inventioneering and the use of a patent machine, these problems are eliminated at this phase of the process. The inventor uses an invention capture system that is synergistic with his or her daily work efforts, and then the patent machine delivers to the triage phase (committee or CPM) a well-written (and drawn) rough draft provisional along with an invention summary report containing analytical decision support metrics. The Invention Summary Report (see example below) uses massive amounts of data from the USPTO and other sources to analyze the submission and provide pertinent predictions on such things as Alice risk, novelty, and obviousness, as well as the likely assignment of the USPTO Art Unit and important associated statistics for that Art Unit. In addition to having a rough draft of the provisional, the committee or CPM now has a consistent and deep view of each invention in summary form, as well as the benefit of analytic comparisons drawn from thousands of patent documents upon which to make a decision.

Here is an example of such a report, as prepared using our company's patent machine:

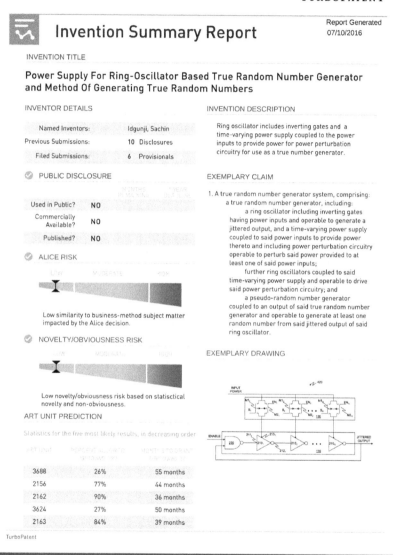

Note that an output of the patent machine—a draft provisional patent—informs the triage decision thoroughly and consistently. Moreover, the document can also be effectively used for the non-patent path. If the decision is to keep the invention as a trade secret, the document serves as a well-enabled description of the invention, one that will pass the trade secret legal test. If the decision is to defensively publish the invention so that no one else can patent it, the draft provisional has sufficient specification to act as prior art. Once published, you don't have to worry about your competition obtaining a patent on this invention that might block your future progress.

In other words, one document with three potential uses (see chart). The production of the document may also reveal other patents that can be purchased or licensed as part of building your portfolio in this technology sector.

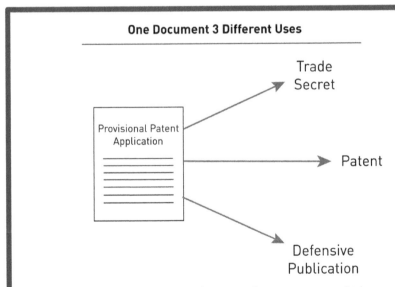

One Document 3 Different Uses

Provisional Patent Application → Trade Secret

Provisional Patent Application → Patent

Provisional Patent Application → Defensive Publication

As this visual shows, how a provisional patent application can serve multiple purposes.

As you will see in the next chapter, pending patent and patent review and triage does not end here, but continues throughout the rest of the Inventioneering process.

In the last chapter, Part I of the Inventioneering process, we looked at the steps to take to determine whether or not to pursue a patent on a new system or method—a process that culminated in the Invention Summary Report. In this chapter, Part II of the Inventioneering process, we will follow the steps to take when that summary report gives the green light to pursuing that patent.

Chapter 15

Inventioneering Process, Part II

But first, a quick look at what should happen to those ideas that don't make the cut.

Too often, the 60 percent or more of invention disclosures that are not approved to be converted to patent applications are left on the cutting room floor, their remaining value discarded. This is a wasteful mistake. There are at least three major problems that can occur when not practicing Inventioneering at this phase of the process.

First, your company may assume that the non-pursued IP constitutes a trade secret. But unless the invention is well-specified and teaches an approach to building the invention, it probably is not a defensible trade secret. The laws pertaining to trade secrets also require the company to protect such secrets and control access to them in some form of a system of record. Unless properly protected, employees may exit your company and use those discarded inventions elsewhere—all the while making subsequent recourse for your company difficult, if not impossible, to achieve.

Second, another company (including one of your competitors) may invent something similar to your discarded invention and successfully pursue a patent. What if you then realize that this invention is now important to your business? Too bad. You're out of luck.

Third, it is a relatively common occurrence among companies with large patent programs that similar inventions are submitted for consideration numerous times over the years. People come and go and the previous disclosures are lost to corporate memory. Usually, the person who has been around the longest says something along the lines of, "I sort of remember someone submitting something similar about four years ago." File now for a patent and you may find that your company has misrepresented inventor-ship, potentially invalidating the asset.

With Inventioneering, a deliberate decision is made early in the process to either keep the invention as a proper trade secret, pursue it as a patent or publish it such that it can serve as prior art inhibiting others from obtaining a patent. In all cases, the invention remains in a database dedicated to tracking the company's prior inventions.

The Path to Patent
The process of publishing or making the invention a trade secret effectively comes to a close at this point. However, the path of pursuing a patent continues. Taking the rough draft provisional produced by a patent machine and either resubmitting it to a patent machine or to a traditional law firm to complete a finished provisional patent application or non-provisional patent application is the next critical step in this journey. The Inventioneering process prescribes that a provisional patent be completed and filed. This produces the quickest results (first to file) and the lowest cost to the initial "patent pending" protection.

While it is important to quickly convert the draft invention disclosure document (draft provisional patent) into a file-able provisional patent, it is also important that the nature of the invention be faithfully captured, otherwise the protection you seek will not be relevant. Furthermore, the Inventioneering drafting approach is to focus on a broad and solid specification, including detailed drawings that are well described. This is best done with the aid of a patent machine to write the full application. That eliminates many of the technical quality errors that will surface as the patent process unfolds.

At this point a Patent Quality Report (see below) is generated and coupled to the patent application for review. A detailed set of patent claims is not essential at this point. When the provisional patent is converted (within the required twelve-month window) to a non-provisional patent application, the Inventioneering prescription is then to file specific and narrow claims covering only one part of the inventive material described in the provisional specification.

There are a couple of benefits to this approach. First, it's easier, cheaper and faster to get narrow claims allowed by the US Patent Office. Additionally, by taking this approach, the patent is less likely to build up problematic "baggage" (see the Prosecution section of this chapter). Second, you have not lost the opportunity to draft and file claims on the remainder of the invention covered in the specification.

A USPTO process known as Continuation allows for new claims to be filed on material that pertains to the remainder of the specification and still enjoy the original priority date of the original provisional filing. This can give your company the advantage of years more time to understand what is actually happening within your company and within the market—and thus allow the newest claims to be drafted with far more data in hand. With Inventioneering, the process focuses upon creating a valuable family of patents comprising both the parent application with the earliest priority date and a set of continuations that also enjoy the earlier priority date. But the claims of Continuation will focus as close as possible on the arc of technology and on products in the market or nearing introduction.

An extreme example of the use of this approach was a company we know that obtained an allowance of grant from the USPTO to a continuation patent while the litigation regarding the parent patent was still underway. Once more, the claims to the newly allowed continuation patent had been steered toward the information provided in the testimony of the infringing party. Now, with the defendant's legal testimony describing its technology and the newly granted claims written with the benefit of that testimony (but yet enjoying the priority date prior to the beginning of the litigation), guess who won? This is powerful stuff.

We hope this helps to convince you that the best way to produce the highest quality and lowest cost patent families is to use a patent machine to complete and validate this work, coupled with expert review by the patent triage committee or assigned patent counsel.

Another reason we advise the use of a patent machine concerns security and legal privilege. Given that the goal of Inventioneering is to create high-quality, defensible patents and trade secrets, it is important to deploy practices that ensure that your inventions are not stolen and, at the same time, that the communication surrounding the development of that IP is held in confidence.

We previously discussed the security mess that plagues traditional patent practice. Using a modern, cloud-based patent machine is a great way to combat direct theft of your IP thanks to the immense and all but unprecedented security measures taken by top-tier cloud service providers. But there is another important, though less well known, advantage as well: with the e-discovery systems now commonly used in litigation, problematic company communications are much easier to obtain. For instance, an email discussion between a patent attorney and one of your inventors would be considered confidential, and covered under the rules of attorney-client privileged communication. But what happens when an email discussion ensues within your company and those emails are forwarded some fourteen times to a multitude of others—and oh yeah, your inventor is quoted as saying something that limits or invalidates the patent?

Email distribution only expands over time. With a patent machine, the communication and collaboration regarding the invention occurs in a single, contained location and then is purged when the patent is granted. Thus, no spurious communication artifacts—i.e., no smoking guns.

Search, File, Accelerate
Inventioneering depends upon a patent machine to provide predictive analytics pertaining to the risk of patentability. These analytics are shared with the CPM or the patent committee and help inform the decision whether or not to proceed to the creation of a full provisional patent application. There is no need to do any additional search at this point in the process. However, prior to the approval to move to the creation and filing of a non-provisional application, a patent machine will generate a more thorough prior art search—a report specifically on the novelty and obviousness of the invention will be generated and used to support the decision to approve the expense of drafting the non-provisional patent application.

In addition, this report will be used as the basis to qualify for an accelerated review process. Accelerating the prosecution has many benefits. We have found that office action cycles are typically decreased, which lowers costs and increases grant rates. Ultimately, the final quality of the patent is increased.

Remember that your company can pay an additional $4,000 to the USPTO to be placed in what is called Track One, which will ensure an office action in one year or less. As we noted earlier, you can think of this as FedEx for patent prosecution. And even though you are paying more upfront, the overall costs tend to be lower.

That said, the Inventioneering process delivers the benefits of acceleration without the additional $4,000 USPTO fee. Why? Because this fee can be avoided if a great deal of the upfront examination is provided by the inventive company. A patent machine can do the work required to satisfy the acceleration requirements as one of its outputs. Now, there are often mitigating circumstances that might cause your CPM or patent committee to choose not to accelerate the examination and prosecution. But the Inventioneering process default should be to accelerate and reap the many benefits of speedier examination.

Prosecute

Once a patent is filed, it enters into the prosecution phase of the journey. Patent prosecution is effectively a review by and negotiation with the US Patent Office.

It is during this back and forth with a patent examiner, usually taking three or more cycles, that an extraordinary amount of patent quality decay and value loss occurs. We call this patent rot.

There are several reasons for patent rot. With the traditional approach, years can go by before the negotiation begins. Meanwhile those responsible for the invention and the drafting of the patent application may have forgotten some of the finer points of the invention. Also, during that time, the inventor might have left the company, the CPM or members of the Patent Committee might have been promoted to different jobs, the patent drafter might have joined a new firm or your company might have fired the firm that wrote the patent application.

Thus, a significant percentage of patent cases today are prosecuted by someone other than the original drafter. The new prosecutor handling this "cold case" must now become as familiar with the invention as he or she can, usually filling in a lot of unknowns with little assistance. The churn of personnel makes for high cost, low quality patents.

And it gets worse. It is at this point in the process that the company's patent quantity goals, combined with the law firm's revenue goals, inevitably result in low-quality, low-value, high-cost patent assets. In other words, the incentives are not aligned with the primary goal of patent quality. Patent practitioners typically are paid for each office action cycle with the patent examiner, and are thought to be successful if they can get something, often anything, granted. It is also true that the monitoring and scrutiny during the prosecution phase of the process is dramatically reduced as compared to the review that occurs prior to filing the original application. As a result of all of the above, errors and omissions occur and new and damaging language is often inserted into the document. This language can dramatically alter the invention, needlessly narrow the claims or create cause for invalidity. All are bad scenarios.

Let us take a moment to point out a general inherent conflict of interest created by the "revolving door" between corporate patent counsel and outside law firms. The implied promise of lucrative partnership positions in law firms keeps in-house counsel wedded to overpriced, inefficient law firms and inhibits them from utilizing, or at least taking the lead on, more efficient and lower-cost alternatives.

Perpetuating The Cycle

Law Firm Attorneys

$$$$$$$$$$$$$$$

Corporate Attorneys

Low-quality Patents

Corporation

Law Firm

A visual depiction of the inherent conflict of interest created by the "revolving door" between corporate patent counsel and the outside law firms who serve them.

This is a big issue for CEOs and CFOs who want to control costs and improve shareholder value and certainty around IP portfolios. It will be up to CEOs and CFOs to ensure impartiality and demand that their IP managers implement lower-cost solutions, at the very least alongside their expensive legacy law firms. Such an implementation will put pressure on the law firms to lower cost and improve quality.

The Inventioneering process counters these flaws, which are inherent in the traditional IP prosecution process. Using a patent machine to monitor, read and analyze each of the office actions and their associated responses, a summary report is generated and delivered to the CPM or patent committee to assist in decision-making responsibilities. This is a powerful reason to employ a patent machine as far upstream in the process as possible. It's a low-cost, automated-patent quality assurance program.

We know of some companies that use automated tools to "secretly" monitor the work product of practitioners who prepare and prosecute their patent applications. This is not consistent with the Inventioneering philosophy. On the contrary, we think that it is in the best interest of patent quality and efficiency to not only provide this technology to practitioners, but also to require that practitioners use and reap the benefits of a patent machine. That said, with Inventioneering, the patent practitioner's performance is also monitored and graded via a Practitioner Scorecard (see below). As President Ronald Reagan famously said, "Trust, but verify."

Practitioner Scorecard

attorney	firm	total applications	attorney allowance rate	allowance rate vs mean	quality score	efficiency metric	review indicator
Malcolm Reynolds	Reynolds, Washburn and Cobb	241	80%	+45%	93	92	✔
Lani Tupu	Warwick Davis	255	56%	+18%	89	88	✔
Ben Sisko	Picard, Sisko and Pike	253	71%	+30%	92	83	✔
Kathryn Mullen	Warwick Davis	220	65%	+27%	90	91	✔
David Greenaway	Warwick Davis	219	61%	+23%	75	89	⚠
Jayne Cobb	Reynolds, Washburn and Cobb	216	55%	+20%	90	91	✔
Don Austen	Warwick Davis	210	61%	+22%	90	86	⚠
Jake Sisko	Picard, Sisko and Pike	205	10%	-30%	42	92	✖
Kristine Kochanski	Kryten Kochanski	204	65%	+30%	74	95	⚠
Arnold Rimmer	Kryten Kochanski	201	48%	-4%	40	77	✖

With Inventioneering, the patent practitioner's performance is monitored and graded via a Practitioner Scorecard.

A patent machine's monitoring of (and reporting on) the in-process patent applications, as well as of the people doing the work, can be done internally at your company. Or you can employ a neutral, third party Patent Quality Assurance Organization.

The advantage of a third party is that it brings an objective viewpoint to the technical quality of the asset being developed and to the responsible practitioners. A third party also frees your employees from doing this work and allows them to focus on the more subjective issues pertaining to fit within your patent business objectives.

Portfolio Management

For our purposes in this book, patent portfolio management deals with technical quality and the pruning of bad assets in order to save millions of dollars in maintenance and legal fees. There have been numerous books written on other aspects of patent portfolio management, including market valuation, licensing and litigation. Our focus here is narrower: Inventioneering is about creating high-quality assets that faithfully capture the inventive concepts produced by your company. Having a technically solid, high-quality patent portfolio will enable you to confidently embark on additional portfolio-related strategies, but we are not covering them here.

With a patent machine providing decision support data to the CPM or the patent committee for every stage of the patent process, it comes down to a "thumbs up" or "thumbs down" decision for each of these steps, as the chart shows:

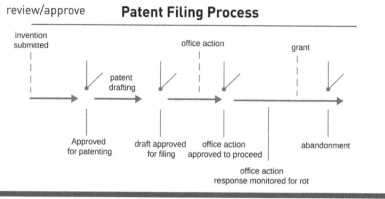

A patent machine provides decision support data throughout the patent process.

Each approval—tacit or explicit—represents a commitment of dollars to be spent on behalf of your company. Thus, it seems like a no-brainer to rigorously monitor this process and ensure that quality is being returned for the money spent. But until now, the data to make these decisions has been absent and the discipline lacking. With Inventioneering, there is no longer an excuse for low-quality patents being marshaled or invalid assets maintained in your portfolio. With a patent-machine-generated Portfolio Report in hand, you must insist that your team use that document in support of meeting your first-year goal of eliminating the worst 10 percent of pending and granted patents.

Inventioneering As a State of Mind

We have now taken you through the entire Inventioneering experience—from the need for a change in your company's attitude towards IP to prepare for the new global competition in patents and trade secrets, to a discussion of how to change your company's culture—from the boardroom on down—in order to become imbued with an Inventioneering culture. We've also covered the steps to supercharge your patent portfolio creation and management using the latest technology tools, including the so-called (and incredibly powerful) patent machine. Below, you'll find a visual that summarizes these IP best practices.

END-TO-END IP BEST PRACTICES

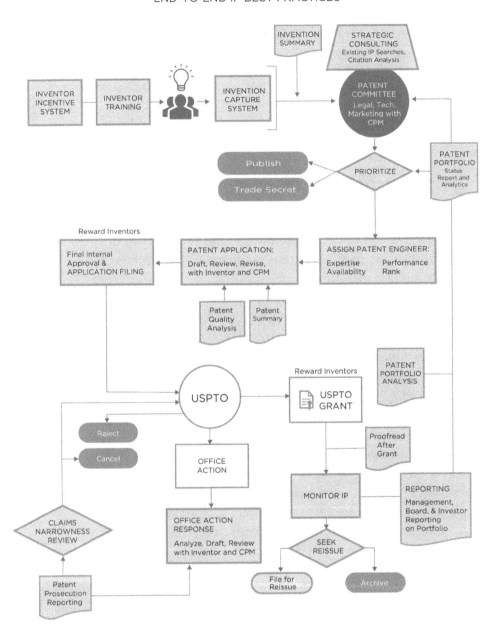

This flow chart outlines best practices from beginning to end of the IP process.

The final step—and the subject of the concluding chapter of this book—will be to look ahead to where the brave new world of global patent competition is heading. We will also take a deeper look at emerging trends in Big Data (including a closer look at patent machines), finance, changing demographics and the rise of patent marketplaces.

> **We end this book with a look at the future of patents and Inventioneering.**

Chapter 16

The Future of Patents

First, however, we must recognize the uniquely contradictory nature of intellectual property.

On the one hand, regarding the creation of intellectual property documents and the legal process, patent law is one of the most conservative and slow-moving industries in the business world. On the other hand, those overseeing it are charged with advising, documenting and processing one of the most forward-thinking and technologically advanced concepts on the planet.

Fundamentally, the ways and means of creating and legally protecting inventions have changed little over the centuries. Yes, the handwritten patent has been replaced, first by the typewritten patent, and then by the word-processor-generated patent. In addition, physical models have been replaced by drawings and textual descriptions. Now, however, we find ourselves at the onset of an industry transformation. In the same way that robotics is revolutionizing manufacturing, technology is turning the field of intellectual property upside down.

While it may be intellectually intriguing to think about the future, in order to run a business it is absolutely essential to have a notion of what's coming, not least because such knowledge provides the opportunity to influence your future. As Apple Computer's Alan Kay once said, "The best way to predict the future is to invent it."

So, let's conclude with a look at six areas where we can see the early stages of impending change impacting various aspects of invention and patents. No surprise that many of these changes are driven by technological advancement. Computers have long exceeded humans when it comes to repetitive and menial tasks, and now they are handling ever more of the intellectual pursuits performed by well-trained professionals. As a result, inventors and patent practitioners will be significantly affected.

This revolution presents both a challenge and an opportunity. The digitization and redefinition of products and services offers a chance to reinvent the very nature of intellectual property and the system used to support it.

Let's now consider what that reinvention might look like.

The Patent Machine

In 1997, Russian chess grandmaster and world champion Gary Kasparov, considered the finest chess player in history, was defeated in a six-game match conducted under strict tournament rules by an IBM supercomputer. Nicknamed Deep Blue, the computer had been designed by a group of Carnegie Mellon students who teamed with IBM Research to take on the challenge of building a machine able to prevail over the world's best chess players. Although Kasparov had beaten an earlier version of Deep Blue a year before, this loss made it clear that no human chess player would ever again defeat the supercomputer.

After Deep Blue's victory, one of its key architects left for Wall Street, and soon after was applying the benefits of supercomputing and big data analytics to stock trading. Ten years later, thanks to advancements in both computer hardware and software, off-the-shelf personal computers had enough power and software sophistication to beat grandmaster chess champions. Then, in 2011, IBM's Watson supercomputer, whose programmers had added natural language processing (NLP) to its arsenal, won the Jeopardy! championship, vanquishing two of the best players in the history of the television game show.

Deep Blue's database contained a history of all the moves of nearly one million grandmaster chess games, any of which it could retrieve during its match with Kasparov. That is a lot of information available to access, but as renowned cognitive researcher Diego Rasskin-Gutman points out in his book, Chess Metaphors, "There are more possible chess games than there are atoms in the universe." Just a few years later, Watson's Jeopardy! victory entailed instant access to more than two hundred million documents representing four terabytes of data as its handle on all of human knowledge. That's also a lot—to say the least—yet still a small fraction of all human knowledge.

By comparison, the accumulated total of granted patents since the very beginning of the United States Patent Office is less than ten million. The current active database of pending and granted patents is about six million. Moreover, patents are, by definition, highly structured documents that must follow a fixed set of rules published by the patent office. Thus, the automation of patenting is a bounded, structured and tractable technical problem. In other words, patent automation is both inevitable and pending.

Using the latest techniques in NLP, machine learning and data analytics, so-called patent machines already are automating many of the tasks required in the drafting, prosecution and assessment of intellectual property. Moreover, the output of this computer automated patenting approach is faster, cheaper and of higher quality than that of even the most seasoned and efficient patent practitioners.

As an example, during a corporate acquisition event, a selling company could easily have five thousand patent assets. Applying a minimal review of two hours per asset, and assuming your company had sixty days to perform the required diligence, you would need to coordinate thirty seasoned patent attorneys and pay about $3 million just for the portfolio assessment. A patent machine delivers a higher quality and more consistent assessment in a single day at orders of magnitude less cost. In short, a human patent master will never beat the patent machine; in fact, the performance gap will only increase.

Patent Financing
A significant portion of business assets are leased or financially leveraged in some way. Although historically this has not been the case for patent portfolios, since 2014 we have seen the emergence of patent financing models that are similar to home mortgages and leases.

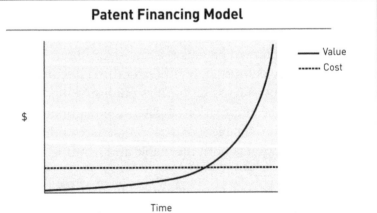

Patent Financing Model

— Value
------- Cost

$

Time

As with home mortgages, the patent financing model allows for the consumer to pay synchronously with the value received.

In this model, the legal and sometimes governmental components of patent development costs are financed by a third party, and the patent asset is used as the collateral for the loan. At this writing, it has been mostly pre-public, early-stage companies that have embraced this model, which is not surprising given that smaller companies have less discretionary capital, and their cost of capital relative to their equity value is very high.

But given that approximately 60 percent of the inventions sourced in larger companies are not pursued as patents (usually due to budget constraints), we believe there is an opportunity for larger companies to also finance some portion of their portfolios. Considering that the short-term costs of developing a patent are much higher than the short-term value of those patents (see chart), it makes sense to find ways to smooth out the costs over time to match the timing of the value received. Also, in the frequent situations in which strategies change or products don't succeed in the marketplace, having less invested in the associated portfolio can be a benefit.

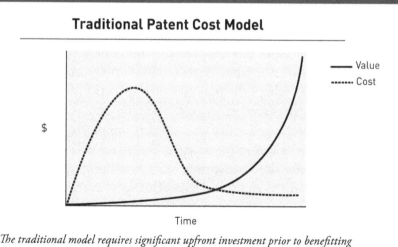

Traditional Patent Cost Model

——— Value
------- Cost

$

Time

The traditional model requires significant upfront investment prior to benefitting from any value.

In practice, the lender holds a lien on the company's IP and the company retains all rights to the patent assets. In the event of a merger or acquisition, these assets are transferable to an acquirer, and the company has the right to buy out the loan at any time. The financier holding the patent asset as collateral is fully aligned with the company with respect to their common desire to create a high-quality asset. In fact, the financing organization takes a very unemotional view of the invention being pursued, which serves as an excellent counterbalance to inventors who may be overly interested in the technology for less than solid business reasons. The savings accrued by utilizing the patent machine and the cost-smoothing financing model will yield a far more accessible patent system. This re-democratization of intellectual property is crucial given the economic reality that 80 percent of corporate market value lies in intangible assets.

A Patent Market

For decades, attempts to create a patent market with the same attributes as the stock market have been pursued and have failed. This may be about to change.

A transparent and robust buying and selling marketplace for IP seems like an obvious, logical and beneficial outcome for all involved. But what exists today is an opaque secondary patent market where the majority of transactions between buyers and sellers are kept secret. The true dynamics that allow for market forces to set prices and keep the playing field a bit more level do not exist for patents. So, if you wish to sell your patents, pricing the asset is more an art—though perhaps more a guessing game—than a science. The same is true for the buyer, as there are few comparable transactions to reference. As far as we can tell, nearly equivalent assets have vastly different market values for no reason other than lack of data.

Unfortunately, there are additional negative consequences to this lack of transparency. Risk assessment becomes extremely difficult in this scenario, which in turn causes otherwise prudent organizations to 1) simply ignore the patent rights of others because they cannot calculate the cost of licensing, or 2) fear that if they approach the rights holder, they will get stuck with an oversized bill. On the flip side, the patent holder, knowing there is no established price for its IP, may ask for the moon simply to get the attention of the target company.

The same holds true in the litigation-award component of the patent legal process. The judge and jury have minimal factual context upon which to base an infringement judgment and royalty. In our opinion, the damage judgments are often shockingly beyond the value of the IP in question.

We believe, given that a patent is a government-granted monopoly, that the public (and most certainly corporate shareholders) should have the equivalent of Freedom of Information Act regulations applied to IP. Especially now, as other nations like China buy up US patent rights, the American public has a right to know what's going on. If a Chinese or Russian company were to offer to buy US federal mineral rights, such as an oil field on federal land, the public would be made aware of that offer. And when a Middle Eastern-based company actually landed a contract to provide services to an East Coast airport, all hell broke loose and the deal was killed. We should treat the disclosure of US patent rights the same way we treat rights surrounding any other federal property.

If it was required that for every IP transaction, including legal settlements, the relevant parties had to disclose the price paid for the assets in the transaction, the entire economy would benefit. Trolls, even those heavily lawyered-up, would be unable to act on the dark fringes of the patent market, and companies would no longer have excuses to ignore the rights of legitimate inventors who deserve to be paid for their innovative work.

Some of this is already happening. Pharmaceutical companies are required to report any settlement with a generic manufacturer of their proprietary drug. Publicly traded companies, where the price of an IP deal is large enough to require disclosure, must do so in a public SEC filing. But such deals are usually so large that it's hard to discern much specific information about the value of a segment of the portfolio, let alone a single asset. It would be like trying to derive the value of your New York City condo from a transaction reported on the purchase of an entire city block.

The trend for corporate IP assets is moving in the direction of corporate financial assets. We predict that this movement will ultimately lead to enhanced transactional transparency in the same way that Sarbanes-Oxley led to greater transparency in the financial markets. And although many fear the fallout from such changes, the only losers would be those who purposefully benefit from the ignorance currently inherent in today's opaque market.

Better Patents with Gender Diversity

In a previous endeavor, we served as executive producers of an award-winning documentary film entitled CODE: Debugging the Gender Gap, and originated and developed the companion resource website www.shescoding.org. CODE documents the significant disparity between the numbers of male versus female software developers employed in American business, and investigates the root causes of this inequality. What we learned from this project is that less than 18 percent of computer science graduates are women, and an even smaller percentage make up the software developer workforce. Similar numbers can be found in nonbiological and chemical technical occupations.

Every study has proved that better and more profitable products are produced by diverse groups, including those that are more gender-inclusive. Most of us have heard the stories of vehicle airbags that were created by all-male product teams and tested on all-male dummies, and that a result of that lopsided testing was that smaller-statured women suffered higher mortality rates when the airbags deployed in accidents. There's a lesson to be learned here when it comes to patents. Given that patents are also a form of product and, in the digital world, will more frequently embody the product itself, the development of patents and patent portfolios would also benefit from increased gender diversity.

If you thought 18 percent was a dismal representation of women in the nonbiological and chemical engineering disciplines, things look far worse when you compare male-to-female inventor ratios in the patent areas of information, communication and technology (together known as ICT, which essentially encompasses everything that is not biological, chemical or pharmaceutical). The data here suggests that women represent less than 5 percent of inventors.

While there are notable and famous exceptions—such as actress Hedy Lamarr, who invented a spread-spectrum communication system for use during World War II, and Dr. Grace Hopper, who invented the COBOL computer programming language—the sad truth is that the world of invention has traditionally been a male-dominated bastion.

Considerable publicity about the problem has resulted in a widespread effort to increase the ranks of female engineers. Signs that the issue is permeating the cultural consciousness is evident in the fact that a few years ago toymaker Mattel came out with Computer Engineer Barbie. Nonetheless, it's clear that there's still a long way to go when it comes to achieving gender parity. The book that Computer Engineer Barbie was based on, for example, was pulled from bookstore shelves after critics noted that story portrayed Barbie as needing the help of boys to make a video game and fix a virus.

The overall trend, however, is positive. Companies and colleges are increasingly focused on growing the ranks of woman in STEM (science, technology, engineering and math) degree programs, while corporations are reporting increased female-to-male ratios in technical jobs. Although a long way from balanced, the numbers are improving. The assumption is that growing the number of women employed in the engineering disciplines in ICT will correspondingly grow the number of female inventors in these technology sectors.

We hope you will endeavor to include women in the next generation of technical employees, those we call Inventioneers. The transformation of your company to a culture of Inventioneering will not be complete unless you do. Your company will benefit if you and your team make the effort to provide women with the coaching and encouragement required to assure their full participation in the invention process.

Patents, Big Data and Financial Market Prediction

Next, let's consider patents and predictions.

In the wake of the 2008 US presidential election, we learned that the most accurate predictors of results were not the pundits, newspapers, pre-election polls or even the statistical averaging of all of those pre-election polls. Instead, the best predictors came from the exchanges set up for people to bet on the outcome of the contest. Why? Because most predictions are encumbered by human bias and blind spots. There is no doubt that pundits, motivated primarily by a need to satisfy their audience, have agendas that distort the accuracy of their predictions.

Patent portfolios are instruments that will benefit from how well they line up with the market future. Patents are a company's bet on future products and services that it believes will be embraced by the market, and a pronouncement of its intent to influence the future. Patents are classic investments that need to earn a return over their 20-year life, and those expected returns economically reflect the intention and direction of products and technologies. Thus, patents are predictions. In the same way that the stock market or a sports book uses the wisdom of the masses—clarified and made bona fide by the backing of actual cash to predict future outcomes—so too can an industry's patenting trends predict which technologies will most likely win versus those that will fade away.

As we discussed previously, your company can measure the activity and monitor the direction the competition is taking by keeping an eye on their patent investments. At a meta-level, you can predict the emergence of new technological directions of an entire industry by keeping watch on its patent class. An example would be the propulsion system of the next generation of personal transportation. Looking back over the past ten years or so, it's clear that patent investments were being made at differing levels in bio-fuels, compressed natural gas, hydrogen fueling and hydrogen electric drive trains, battery electric vehicles, and gas/electric hybrid powered vehicles. Knowing that the patent cost itself is about $60,000 and that it typically represents about fifty times that amount in actual R&D spending, you can see that the wisdom of the crowd—in this case a very knowledgeable crowd made up of industry players—was already predicting the winners and losers of this particular technology race.

That said, not all of an industry's investment is represented by its patent portfolios, since some inventions may be held as trade secrets or never committed to the patent process. Nonetheless, when it comes to predicting emerging technologies, it's a good idea to focus attention on where your toughest competitors are filing significant amounts of IP.

Big data analytics are already in use by the investment community. If your company is betting against the trends, you should be prepared to defend your minority position relative to the momentum of the rest of the industry. At this juncture, for example, we would not want to defend continued investment in compressed natural gas as a means of personal transportation.

Expect to see a lot more predictions using patent information crunched by big data analytics in the years to come. Including predictions about your own company.

The Future Patent System

In Chapter 1 we discussed a future where everything will have been "Napsterized." We're looking toward a digital world where, as today with software, books and music, almost all products and services can be delivered electronically. If it's a physical good, then the digital representation will be instantly and locally transformed into its physical manifestation. In this new era, the invention, and the patent that protects the invention, will be embodied in digital information.

In the software industry today, there are differing models for the protection, distribution and usage of code. The open source model allows for the intellectual property and work-product of another to be shared and freely used by others. There are server hubs that act as directories and repositories for open source software.

Many companies use such open source software and then build proprietary value on top of the free code. But there are many forms of license agreements that bring confusion as to what encumbrances might come with this usage. One license might negate your company's ability to use the software and build exclusive and proprietary value into it. Another might require you to contribute to the community any enhancements that you make to the code. Still another bit of code might have used content from a standards body that requires payment for use. The industry has become so confusing, and operating within it so risky, that there are now businesses offering automated systems that will grind through your software to identify any misuse of another's technology.

We believe that the patent system will evolve to become a digital repository for all patent-protected digital inventions. As you will recall, during the Industrial Age the United States Patent Office required a working model or prototype of any invention someone was attempting to patent. That practice was curtailed for two reasons. First, all of those working models filled warehouses to overflowing (not to mention the fact that they were difficult to transport to the patent office). Second, the inventions themselves evolved to become too complicated to practicably represent in a physical form.

In the digital age, neither of these problems apply. Digital information representing the invention requires effectively zero physical space and any complexity would be discernible in the decompilation of the information (for example, in a 3D printout). Therefore, the opportunity exists for the patent office to reinstate the requirement of a "working model," which would be comprised of the digital embodiment of the invention.

In the digital era patent system, understanding the novelty of an invention (that is, searching for prior art) will be much easier. An AI system will effectively search the PTO database as well as other non-patent material. Everyone, including trolls, will be required to build digital implementations of their patented inventions. Those implementations, like the physical prototypes once required by the USPTO, will provide useful starting points for those wishing to license and use the invention. Licensing will be greatly simplified and awards in patent legal disputes easier to calculate.

We conclude this book with a review of eight crucial points that we want you to walk away with:

1. The world is on its way to becoming "Napsterized" —that is, a predominantly digital world where, as today with software, books and music, almost all products and services can be delivered electronically. Operational barriers to entry in business are rapidly disappearing, leaving legal barriers (IP) as the sole enduring barrier. Because of this, intellectual property will emerge as the most valuable corporate asset.

2. Your competitors, from other companies to other countries (such as China), understand the importance of IP and are taking it very seriously. As a corporate leader, you need to be equally concerned and taking action right now.

3. There are emerging risks related to intellectual property—beyond competitive companies and countries—that many executives fail to understand. As a corporate leader, you must be aware of shareholder risks, board of director accountability and spurious lawsuits. It is no longer sufficient to say "It's complicated" or "Legal has got this" when it comes to your company's IP and the associated liabilities.

4. Quality patents are a proxy for a multitude of positive markers in a company. Investors and

industry analysts have historically equated strong patent holdings to company value, endurance, longevity, innovation and strong, smart leadership.

5. The intellectual property industry and its processes have long been broken, and patent law is in a constant state of change. As a result, your portfolio is a dynamic asset that must be regularly monitored, pruned and curated. Your patent portfolio likely contains a lot of junk, on which you are wasting money in maintenance costs. Worse, your junk-filled portfolio is giving you a false sense of security.

6. Although intellectual property law has historically been seen as an arcane, low-tech, painfully slow, complicated and expensive field, there are now automated technologies that alleviate many of these issues. These systems, which you should be incorporating into your IP processes, allow corporate executives to quickly and easily understand, manage and measure patents and IP portfolios.

7. In order for an enterprise to survive in this new business era, it is no longer sufficient to leave your company's intellectual property solely in the hands of your legal team. Understanding and leading your company's IP efforts is an essential role for the executive team and board of directors.

8. In order for your business to win in this new era, you must go even further. You must look to Inventioneering—a set of best and enhanced practices that start at the very top of your company's hierarchy and permeate throughout the business. Inventioneering begins with every product's conception and continues to the end of its lifecycle. To successfully utilize Inventioneering, you must work to embed it into the very culture of your company.

The time has come for you and your organization to embrace Inventioneering as the new source of advantage over your competitors. We've shown that rather than being legalistic and boring, IP has become one of the most exciting and challenging new battlegrounds in global competition. In fact, far from being arcane and confusing, IP is a lot like the rest of the business world. It comes complete with competitive strategies, tactics, market-making possibilities, trading, and unexpected threats and opportunities. It will provide you with at least as much of a challenge as any other part of your business. And at this time in history, it's more important than ever.

Most of all, we hope that we have driven home the fact that the time to act on your IP strategy is now. Whether you've already experienced them or not, threats to your company—in the form of patent trolls, competitors, even entire nations—are emerging from every direction, and they are gearing up for a fight. There is no pretending that they aren't there—far from it, since they are coming for you. It's time to fight back.

**Good luck.
And if you need help, contact us.**

We've got your back.

Notes

[1] Brian Fung, "Patent trolls now account for 67 percent of all new patent lawsuits," The Washington Post, (July 15, 2014).

[2] "Apple sues Samsung for $2bn as tech rivals head back to court," The Guardian (March 31, 2014).

[3] IPR does not just allow arguments pertaining to prior art, but also other means for invalidity such as concluding that the patent was not allowable patent material (101 rejection). This is how Alice is being used to negate previously granted software and business process patents as "abstract" or vague.

[4] Jim McTague, "Kyle Bass' Comeback Plan: Oil, Argentina and Patents," Barron's (August 13, 2015).

[5] Edward Wyatt, "Obama Orders Regulators to Root Out 'Patent Trolls,'" New York Times, (June 4, 2013).

[6] Joff Wild, "IP-savvy activist shareholders + declining patent values + tightening patent eligibility = potential trouble for public companies," IAM, (January 26, 2015).

[7] Nick Hanauer and Eric Beinhocker, "Capitalism Redefined," Democracy: A Journal of Ideas, No. 31, Winter 2014, p. 34.

[8] http://www.the-business-of-patents.com/us-patents.html

[9] Ian D McClure and Elvir Causevic, "Board Accountability for Patents," Intellectual Asset Management (Nov/Dec 2015, p. 43).

[10] Ibid.

[11] Ibid, pg. 46.

[12] Ibid, pg. 50.

[13] Smith v. Van Gorkom.

[14] Marius Melad, "Patent Insurance: Pricey, But May Be Worth It," Law360, February 3, 2006.

[15] Ibid.

[16] Ibid.

[17] Source: brainyquotes.com

Bibliography
Works Consulted

Aaker, David. Brand Relevance: Making Competitors Irrelevant. San Francisco: Jossey-Bass, 2011. Print.

Adams, Dylan O. Patents Demystified: An Insider's Guide to Protecting Ideas and Inventions. American Bar Association, 7 Dec 2015. Print.

Baer, Drake, and Nudelman, Mike. "25 Popular Business Books Summarized In One Sentence Each." www.businessinsider.com. Business Insider. 28 May 2014. Web. 2016.

Bandy, Crystal M. Intellectual Property as an Emerging Asset Class: Strategy and Management. Washington: Lakeside Capital Group, 2015. Print.

Berger, Warren. A More Beautiful Question: The Power of Inquiry to Spark Breakthrough Ideas. New York: Bloomsbury, 2014. Print.

Bercovici, Jeff. "Five Top VCs Pick the Ten Biggest Tech Trends of the Next Five Years." www.forbes.com. n.p. 30 May 2014. Web. 2016. "Best Practices: Intellectual Property Protection in China." www.uschina.org. The US-China Business Council. n.d. Web. 2016. "Black Stone IP: Company Overview." www.blackstoneip.com. Black Stone IP, LLC. Mar 2015. Web. 2016.

Blaxill, Mark, and Eckardt, Ralph. The Invisible Edge: Taking Your Strategy to the Next Level Using Intellectual Property.

New York: Penguin, 2009. Print.

www.brainyquote.com. BrainyQuote. n.d. Web. 2016.

Campbell, Anita. "What the Rise in Lawsuits Means to Your Small Business." www.openforum.com. n.p. 16 Nov 2012. Web. 2016.

Chen, Tony, et al. "Real and Present Danger: Patent Litigation in China." www.law360.com. Portfolio Media. 5 Jun 2009. Web. 2016.

Chien, Colleen. "Patent Assertion and Startup Innovation." www.newamerica.org. New America Foundation. Sept 2013. Web. 2016.

"China: Effects of Intellectual Property Infringement and Indigenous Innovation Policies on the U.S. Economy." www. usitc.gov. U.S. International Trade Commission. May 2011. Web. 2016.

"China's IQ (Innovation Quotient): Trends in Patenting and the Globalization of Chinese Innovation." www. ip.thomsonreuters.com. Thomson Reuters. 2014. Web. 2016.

"The Constitution of the United States." www.constitutionus. com. n.p. n.d. Web. 2016."Copyrights and Patents: Annotation 39-Article 1." www.constitution.findlaw.com. n.p. 12 Oct 2016. Web. 2016.

Courtchouladze, Elena. "Global IP Registration Increases; China at Forefront of IP Filings." www.ip-watch.org. Intellectual Property Watch. 17 Dec 2014. Web. 2016.

Decker, Susan. "VirnetX to Vringo's Lost Millions Show Patent Peril." www.bloomberg.com. Bloomberg. 16 Sep 2014. Web. 2016.

Demmitt, Jacob. "Amazon makes Thomas Reuters' List of top innovators for the first time, IBM drops off." www.geekwire. com. n.p. 12 Nov 2015. Web. 2016.

DeRuyck, Josephine. "EPO Hits New Record in Patent Filings; US, China Rise." www.ip-watch.org. Intellectual Property Watch. 03 Mar 2015. Web. 2016.

Domb, Ellen. www.trizrealworld.blogspot.com. n.p. 10 Oct 2013. Web. 2016.

Economics and Statistics Administration, and U.S. Patent and Trademark Office. "Intellectual Property and the U.S. Economy: 2016 Update." www.uspto.gov. U.S. Patent and Trademark Office. Sept 2016. Web. 2016.

Eichenwald, Kurt and McCabe, Sean. "The Great Smartphone War." www.vanityfair.com. Conde Nast. June 2014. Web. 2016.

"Evolve or Perish: Legal Tech at the Center of Patent Darwinism." www.innography.com. n.p. 10 Nov 2015. Webinar. 2016.

Frenkel, Karen. "The Reporting Gap on the Patent Gender Gap." www.cacm.acm.org. Association for Computing Machinery. 30 May 2013. Web. 2016.

Fricke, Peter. "Chinese Patent-Infringer Backs U.S. Patent Reform." www.dailycaller.com. n.p. 5 May 2015. Web. 2016.

Frohwein, Robert J., and Smith, Gregory Scott. The Pocket Idiot's Guide to Patents. Pennsylvania: Alpha Publishing, 7 Dec 2004. Print.

Gallagher, Billy. "A Tale of Two Patents: Why Facebook Can't Clone Snapchat." www.techcrunch.com. AOL Inc. 22 Jun 2014. Web. 2016.

Goldstein, Larry M. Litigation-Proof Patents: Avoiding the Most Common Patent Mistakes. True Value Press, 29 Oct 2014. Print.

Goldstein, Larry M. Patent Portfolios: Quality, Creation, and Cost. True Value Press, 2015. Print.

Goldstein, Larry M. True Patent Value. True Value Press, 2013. Print.

Gollin, Michael A. Driving Innovation: Intellectual Property Strategies for a Dynamic World. New York: Cambridge University Press, 2008. Print.

Graham, Stuart et al. "High Technology Entrepreneurs and the Patent System: Results of the 2008

Berkeley Patent Survey." www.scholarship.law.berkeley.edu. Berkeley Technology Law Journal. 16 Apr 2010. Web. 2016.

Graham, Stuart and Sichelman, Ted. "Patenting by Entrepreneurs: An Empirical Study." www.papers.ssrn.com. Michigan Telecommunications and Technology Law Review, Vol. 17, pp. 111-180. 6 Sep 2010. eLibrary. 2016.

Graupner, Hardy. "China Drives Growth in Patent Filings." www.dw.com. Deutsche Welle. 14 Dec 2015. Web. 2016.

Harper, Alan. "China's Patent Targets for 2020." www.walkermorris.co.uk. Walker Morris, LLP. 2 Mar 2015. Web. 2016.

Harrison, Suzanne S., and Sullivan, Patrick H. Edison in the Boardroom Revisited: How Leading Companies

Realize Value from Their Intellectual Property. New Jersey: John Wiley & Sons, Inc., 2011. Print.

Huang, Qian and Devinsky, Paul. "China-Home and Away: The Next IP Powerhouse." www.law360.com. Portfolio Media. 21 Oct 2009. Web. 2016.

Hunt, Jennifer et al. "Why Don't Women Patent?" www.nber. org. The National Bureau of Economic Research. May 2013. Web. 2016.

"IBM Annual Report 2015." www.ibm.com. International Business Machines Corporation. 23 Feb 2016. Web. 2016.

"Idea Creation, Reward System Tracking and IP Management." www.youtube.com. Innovation Asset Group. 7 Aug 2012. Web. 2016. www.ideationtriz.com. Ideation International Inc. 13 Jan 2012. Web. 2016.

"Infographics." www.boltinsurance.com. n.p. n.d. Web. 2016.

"Innovation Economy Outlook 2016." www.SVB.com. SVB Financial Group. n.d. Web. 2016.

www.ipglossary.com. Origin Ltd. 2006-2013. Web. 2016.

www.ipo.org. Intellectual Property Owners Association. n.d. Web. 2016.

www.ipwatchdog.com. IP Watchdog. 1999-2016. Web. 2016.

Kennedy, John F. "Inaugural Address." www.izquotes.com. n.p. 20 Jan 1961. Web. 2016.

Krajec, Russell. Investing in Patents: Everything a Startup Investor Needs to Know. Colorado: BlueIron, LLC., 2016. Print.

Lee, Aileen. "Welcome to The Unicorn Club: Learning from Billion-Dollar Startups." www.techcrunch.com. AOL Inc. 2 Nov 2013. Web. 2016.

Lee, Mitchelle. "USPTO to Launch a Glossary Pilot Program that Will Support a Better Patent System." www.uspto.gov. United States Patent and Trademark Office. 12 Jun 2014. Web. 2016.

www.lexmachina.com. Lex Machina. n.d. Web. 2016.

Loney, Michael. "The Options for Alternative Patent Licensing Compared." www.managingip.com. n.p. 10 Jun 2014. Web. 2016.

www.lotnet.com. n.p. n.d. Web. 2016.

Marandett, Eric J., and Chen, Fangli. "Taming the Wild West of IP Protection." www.law360.com. Portfolio Media. 18 Feb 2011. Web. 2016.

Marco, Alan, et al. "Perspectives on the growth in Chinese patent applications to the USPTO." www.uspto.gov. United States Patent and Trademark Office. Feb 2014. Web. 2016

Markides, Constantinos. "Strategic Innovation." www.sloanreview.mit.edu. Massachusetts Institute of Technology. 15 Apr 1997. Web. 2016.

Martin, John. "China's "Patent Island" Deserves a Second Look." www.rdmag.com. R&D Magazine Online. 4 Sep 2015. Web. 2016.

Masnick, Mike. "China's Patent Strategy Strategy Isn't About Innovation; It's an Economic Weapon Against Foreign Companies." www.techdirt.com. n.p. 4 Jan 2011. Web. 2016.

McClure, Ian. "Accountability in the Patent Market: A Duty to Monitor Patent Risk from the Boardroom." www.digitalcommons.law.scu.edu. Santa Clara High Technology Law Journal, Vol. 31, pp. 218-250. eLibrary. 2016.

McClure, Ian and Causevic, Elvir. "Board Accountability for Patents." www.IAM-media.com. Globe Business Media Group. 1 Oct 2015. Web. 2016.

"More Women Obtaining Patents, Trademarks in Recent Years." www.nwbc.gov. National Women's Business Council. 1 Mar 2012. Web. 2016.

"The Most Innovative Companies 2013." www.bcgperspectives.com. The Boston Consulting Group. September, 2013. Web. 2016.

Musk, Elon. "All Our Patent Are Belong To You." www.tesla.com. n.p. 12 June 2014. Web. 2016.

"National Patent Development Strategy (2011-2020)."

http://graphics8.nytimes.com/packages/pdf/business/SIPONatPatentDevStrategy.pdf. n.p., n.d., Web. 2016.

Neumeyer, Chris. "China's Great Leap Forward in Patents." www.ipwatchdog.com. n.p. 4 Apr 2013. Web. 2016.

Palfrey, John. Intellectual Property Strategy. Massachusetts: The MIT Press, 2012. Print.

Pan, Susan P. "Tips for Successful IP Collaboration in China." www.law360.com. Portfolio Media. 10 Sept 2013. Web. 2016.

www.patentcore.com. LexisNexis PatentAdvisor. 7 May 2013. Web. 2016.

"Patent growth hits two-decade record in 2012". www.wipo.int. World Intellectual Property Organization. n.d. Web. 2016.

"2013 Patent Litigation Study: Big cases make headlines, while patent cases proliferate" www.us.pwc.com. PriceWaterhouseCoopers, LLP. 2013. Web. 2016.

Perkowski, Jack. "Protecting Intellectual Property Rights in China." www.forbes.com. n.p. 18 Apr 2012. Web. 2016.

Plotkin, Robert. The Genie in the Machine: How Computer-Automated Inventing is Revolutionizing Law and Business. California: Stanford University Press, 2009. Print.

Quinn, Gene. "The Cost of Obtaining a Patent in the U.S." www.ipwatchdog.com. n.p. 4 Apr 2015. Web. 2016.

Ramadan, Al. Play Bigger: How Pirates, Dreamers, and Innovators Create and Dominate Markets. New York: HarperCollins Books, 2016. Print.

Reisinger, Don. "Apple wins patents on Game Center, iPhone Burst Mode" www.cnet.com. CBS Interactive Inc. 27 May 2014. Web. 2016.

Reitzig, Markus. "How Executives Can Enhance IP Strategy and Performance." www.sloanreview.mit.edu. Massachusetts Institute of Technology. 1 Oct 2007. Web. 2016.

"Remarks by Chairman Alan Greenspan: Intellectual Property Rights." www.federalreserve.gov. Federal Reserve Board. 27 Feb 2004. Web. 2016.

"Report on Patent Enforcement in China." www.uspto.gov. U.S. Patent and Trademark Office. 13 Jun 2012. Web. 2016.

www.richardsonoliver.com. Richardson Oliver Law Group, LLP. 2014-2016. Web. 2016.

Robinson, Erick. "China Increasing Patent Rights as U.S. Goes the Other Way." www.law360.com. Portfolio Media, Inc. 22 Oct 2015. Web. 2016.

Rothschild, David. "Forecasting Elections: Comparing Prediction Markets, Polls, and Their Biases." www.poq.oxfordjournals.org. Oxford University Press. 2009. Web. 2016.www.rpxcorp.com. RPX Corporation. n.d. Web. 2016.

Saez, Catherine. "International Patent Filings Begin to Bounce Back; China Rocketing, U.S. at Half-Mast." www.ip-watch. org. Intellectual Property Watch. 9 Feb 2011. Web. 2016.

Schotter, Andreas and Teagarden, Mary. "Protecting Intellectual Property in China." www.sloanreview.mit.edu. Massachusetts Institute of Technology. 17 Jun 2014. Web. 2016.

Sessions, Britten. "Patent Practice Skills and Strategies." Online: www.lulu.com, 2013. Print.

Shuchman, Lisa. "China Powers to No. 1 in the World Patent Filing Race." www.corpcounsel.com. ALM Media Properties, LLC., 14 Dec 2015. Web. 2016.

Silver, Nate. The Signal and the Noise: Why So Many Predictions Fail – But Some Don't. New York: Penguin Books, 3 Feb 2015. Print.

Simonite, Tom. "Technology Stalled in 1970." www. technologyreview.com. MIT Technology Review. 18 Sep 2014. Web. 2016.

Sneddon, Michael. "Inside Views: A Look at the Huge Upswing in China Patent Filings." www.ip-watch.org. Intellectual Property Watch. 22 Apr 2015. Web. 2016.

Soper, Taylor. "How Portland's public transit mobile ticket app maker recovered after being sued for patent infringement." www.geekwire.com. 16 May 2014. Web. 2016.2011. Web. 2016.www.stratnews.com. Strategic News Service LLC. n.d. Web. 2016.

"Table 1 Distribution of Applications for Inventions Received from Home and Abroad." www.english.sipo.gov.cn. State Intellectual Property Office of the P.R.C., 11 Feb 2014. Web. 2016.

"Top 10 Strangest Patents." www.sciencechannel.com. n.p. n.d. Web. 2016. www.turbopatents.us. TurboPatent Corp. n.d. Web. 2016.

"US Patents-A Brief History" www.the-business-of-patents.com. The Business of Patents. 2006-2015. Web. 2016.

"U.S. Supreme Court Case Diamond v. Diehr." www.bitlaw. com. Beck Tysver Evans. n.d. Web. 2016.

Walter, Skip. "Patent Analytics and Matching Software" www. factor10x.com. Factor, Inc. 12 Nov 2013. Web. 2016.

Warner, Eric. "Patenting and Innovation in China: Incentives, Policy, and Outcomes." www.rand.org. RAND Corporation. Nov 2014. Web. 2016.

www.wipo.int. World Intellectual Property Organization. n.d. Web. 2016.

Zhang, Alex. "Key Considerations for Patent Strategies in China." www.ipwatchdog.com. n.p. 6 Nov

Bibliography
Works Cited

Apple sues Samsung for $2bn as tech rivals head back to court," The Guardian (March 31, 2014).

Brian Fung, "Patent trolls now account for 67 percent of all new patent lawsuits," The Washington Post, (July 15, 2014).

Democracy: A Journal of Ideas, No. 31, Winter 2014, p. 34.

Edward Wyatt, "Obama Orders Regulators to Root Out 'Patent Trolls,'" New York Times, (June 4, 2013).

Ian D McClure and Elvir Causevic, "Board Accountability for Patents," Intellectual Asset Management (Nov/Dec 2015, p. 43).

Jim McTague, "Kyle Bass' Comeback Plan: Oil, Argentina and Patents," Barron's (August 13, 2015).

Joff Wild, "IP-savvy activist shareholders + declining patent values + tightening patent eligibility = potential trouble for public companies," IAM, (January 26, 2015).

Marius Melad, "Patent Insurance: Pricey, But May Be Worth It," Law360, February 3, 2006.

Nick Hanauer and Eric Beinhocker, "Capitalism Redefined".

Index

C

calculus, 34, 105
Carnegie Mellon students, 234
century patent law, 87
CEO Patent Report, 135–39,
  141, 143, 145, 147, 149,
  151, 153, 155, 157, 159,
  161, 163, 165, 177–78
challengers, 41, 194–96, 211
China, 5, 18, 21–27, 29,
  141, 143, 239, 246
  patent filings in, 25
Chinese companies, 24, 26
claims, 24, 34, 39, 42–43,
  56, 60, 102, 104, 118,
  193, 222, 225
cloud-based system, 204
CLS Bank, 88
Cobb, Jayne, 159, 170
committee, patent
  triage, 213, 222
company, startup, 122, 188
company culture, 114,
  180–81, 183
company inventions, 212
company IP, 107, 116
company portfolio, 139, 141
company's IP, 94, 113,
  133, 137, 238, 246
Congress, 41, 80, 82, 87
core business, 38, 186, 188
corporate patent practice,
  common, 202
corporations, 34, 48, 64–65,
  68–69, 98, 117, 125–27, 158,
  184, 188, 200–201, 242
costs, 4–6, 14–15, 68–69,
  71–72, 123, 126, 146,
  156, 166, 180, 182, 185,

224, 236–37, 239
counsel, 70, 98, 102, 134,
  146, 159, 163, 165, 167–68
courts, 20, 23–24, 27,
  32, 37–41, 47, 56, 83,
  86, 102, 119, 186
CPM (corporate patent
  manager), 213–14,
  223–25, 227–28
Crichton, John, 170
Cultural Audit, 138, 169
culture
  company's, 229
  new invention, 126
  non-Inventioneering, 214
Customers and Patent
  Appeals, 86

D

data analytics, 99–100, 129,
  180–81, 199, 235, 244
Deep Blue, 234–35
defendant, 186, 222
Defensive Patent
  Strategy, 160, 185
Deming, 14, 16, 28
Direct Acquisition, 139–40
discipline, 95, 133, 183, 229
disclosure, 117–18, 163, 168,
  174, 213, 220, 239–40
Dodd-Frank, 117
Dow Chemical, 83

E

Edison, Thomas, 59, 82
employee invention

submissions, 165
employee participation, 172
employee participation level, 172
employees, participating, 172
Enhanced Competitor,
   18, 21, 23, 25, 27, 29
entities, non-practicing,
   32–36, 186
Epstein, Solomon, 170
errors, 102, 200–201, 225
Essential Corporate
   Resource, 92, 95, 97, 99,
   101, 103, 105, 107, 109
examinations, 68, 70, 104, 224

F

Facebook, 7, 55, 158
Federal Trade Commission, 33
FedEx, 61, 224
fees, legal, 37, 146, 186, 228
filed patent application, 202
file patent applications, 98, 211
Financial Market
   Prediction, 242
first-inventor-to-file
   system, 41, 59
First to File, 59
Frye, Kaylee, 170
FTC report, 37

G

Gaeta, Felix, 170
General Electric, 83
goals, 6, 24, 42, 77, 80, 114,
   121, 128, 166, 181–83,
   206, 209, 222, 229

primary, 160, 225
granted patents, 43, 73, 102,
   147, 182, 203, 229, 235
Granted patents and pending
   applications by country, 141
Granted Portfolio Value, 145
grants, company's patent, 66
Graphics Processing, 156

H

Hewlett-Packard, 36, 89
Hopkins, Samuel, 80
Hopper, Grace, 241
human problems, 78

I

IBM, 33, 83, 89, 98,
   126, 158, 187
IBM's Watson, 199
Icahn, Carl, 24
idea-to-innovation-to-
   invention process, 47
IDF (invention disclosure
   form), 148, 161, 172
implementations, 73, 226, 246
Industrial Age, 245
Industrial Property, 23
Industrial Revolution, 26
Information Security, 156
infringement, 33–34,
   44, 84–85, 97, 187
in-process patent
   applications, 228
insurance, 122–23
Intellectual Asset
   Management, 116

K

L

P

Palmisano, Samuel J., 126
Parker, Sean, 7
patentability, 41, 61,
  87, 163, 168, 223
Patent Act, 57, 80, 99
patent activist
  shareholders, 44–45
patent appication, 172
patent application
  given, 68
  initial, 101
  non-provisional, 220–21, 223
patent application devolves, 134
patent application
  process, 69, 82
patent application
  review process, 69
patent applications, 58–59, 61–
  62, 69–72, 82–83, 115–16,
  140, 148, 169, 171, 192–93,
  210, 219, 221, 225, 227
patent approval process, 86
patent assets, 105, 136,
  147, 236–38
patent asset value, 117
patent attorney, 20, 60, 83, 223
patent automation, 207, 235
patent basics, 54, 63
patent budget, 161
patent cases, 34, 37, 225
patent committee, 165,
  223–25, 227–28
Patent Cooperation
  Treaty. See PCT
patent costs, 70, 243
patent counsel, 98, 182, 202
  corporate, 226
patent creation, 203, 208

Patent Economics, 64,
  67, 69, 71, 73, 75
patent examiner, 101–2, 224–25
Patent Filing Process, 61
patent filings, 25, 48, 86, 93,
  97–98, 103, 115, 121, 181
patent holders, 41–42, 86, 239
patent holdings, 34, 44, 112
patent information, 117–18, 244
patent infringement, 24,
  31, 95, 117, 119, 122
patenting, 89, 163,
  165, 213, 235
patent insurance, 111,
  116, 119, 122–23
patent law, 41, 59, 84, 87,
  104, 123, 192, 233, 247
patent lawsuits, 33–34, 36, 38
patent licensing, 33, 67
patent litigation, 39, 83, 117, 119
patent litigation costs, 35
patent machine, 198, 200–201,
  210, 214, 216, 220–24,
  226–29, 231, 234–36, 238
Patent Machines and Secure
  Systems, 198, 201, 203, 205
patent managers, 70,
  135, 163, 182
patent market, 238, 240
patent office, 41, 59, 81–82,
  86, 88, 102, 207, 235, 245
Patent Portfolio Report,
  100–101
patent portfolios, 45, 47,
  83–84, 86, 89, 105–7, 119,
  122–23, 125, 128, 160, 166,
  199–200, 241, 243–44
patent practitioners, 104,
  182, 200, 225, 234
patent process, 68, 73,
  96, 171, 200, 207, 214,

Q

R

US patent portfolio costs, 134
US patent rights, 239
USPTO (United States Patent
and Trademark Office),
60–62, 65, 69, 72, 81, 115,
196, 201, 214, 222, 224, 246
USPTO Fees, 70, 134,
150–54, 224

V

value, 43–44, 47, 54–55, 89,
92–95, 98, 104–7, 112–13,
118–19, 123, 126, 134–36,
193–94, 236–37, 239–40
Value Creation, 76, 79,
81, 83, 85, 87, 89, 91
value of patents, 104–5, 117

Z

Zander, 96

W

war
competitive, 24
global IP, 28
great chip, 15
new, 85
Watson's Jeopardy, 235
WIPO (World Intellectual
Property Organization), 23
women, 240–42
World Intellectual Property
Organization (WIPO), 23
World War II, 14, 84, 241
World Wide Web, 7

JAMES BILLMAIER

About the Authors

J ames Billmaier has devoted his professional life to predicting how emerging technologies and business models will impact companies in the future. His previous works and accomplishments have gained him a reputation for being astonishingly accurate.

Billmaier is the Co-Founder and CEO of Seattle based TurboPatent Corporation, an Artificial Intelligence (AI) software company whose mission is to automate the patent process, thereby increasing patent quality while dramatically reducing cost.

Prior to founding TurboPatent Corporation, James served as Chairman and CEO of three highly successful software technology companies: Click2Learn, which he led to an IPO in 1998, Digeo Inc., where he and his team won back-to-back EMMY awards for technical achievement, and Melodeo Inc., a cloud-based media platform company which was acquired by Hewlett Packard in 2010.

Billmaier was previously Vice President of Sun Microsystems Networking Software Division in the Bay Area, where he led the development and marketing teams behind Sun's first Internet offerings.

He also served as Vice President of Software Marketing and Business Development at MIPs Computer Systems.

Companies under Billmaier's leadership have filed for over 700 patent applications, and Billmaier himself is the inventor of more than 100 patent filings. He serves as a committee member of the Intellectual Property Owners (IPO) Association.

Billmaier has spent much of his life studying ingenuity and innovation. All that he has learned about the best practices for deploying powerful IP business strategies informs this important and timely book.

File photo, 2017.

About the Authors

File photo, 2017.

Britt Griffith has always been passionate about invention, having earned her first granted patent at the age of 15.

Britt graduated from Stanford University with Bachelors and Masters degrees in Digital Media. Her graduate research included designing and running many studies in Stanford's Virtual Human Interaction Lab. She received Academic All-American honors and graduated first in her graduate program.

Britt has been TurboPatent's Senior Director of Marketing since 2013. Prior to joining TurboPatent, Britt was a contributing writer to the Pulitzer Prize-winning team at the San Francisco Chronicle. She was an Executive Producer of the film CODE: Debugging the Gender Gap, and is the Co-Founder of She's Coding, an organization committed to diversifying the technology workforce.

ABOUT
WINDRUSH PUBLISHERS

Dallas, Texas

Founded in Dallas, Texas, WindRush Publishers excels at bringing books of exceptional quality and content to the minds of discriminating readers everywhere. With an eye for excellence we always are on the search for new inspirational and motivational topics by expert authors in a variety of subjects.

WindRush is the publisher of the award-winning and bestselling books: Running Toward Danger, My Fellow Americans, Lizard Bites & Street Riots, along with the Amazon Top 100 ranked Four Percent.

Stay Informed and Inspired at:
www.WindRushPub.com

Notes

Notes

Notes